All Together Now

records, instructions and wishes for those you love

Elaine Todd

First Edition

Blazing Star Press
1805 Main Street Suite A
Lafayette, Indiana 47904

All Together Now

**Putting together
the puzzle pieces of your life.**

Emergency Medical

Family History and Stories

Final Arrangements

Financial Records

Healthcare

Household Information

Location of Important Documents

Personal Data

And much, much more . . .

Edited by Katalina Miskey-Gilp
Carol Bloom of Bloom Ink
Cover design and illustrations by Beth Elzer.
Interior design by Anita Noble.

Reprints of quotes taken from "The Employee Handbook of New Work Habits in a Radically Changing World" and "A Survival Guide to the Stress of Organizational Change," by Price Pritchett and Ron Pound, are used with full permission of Pritchett & Associates with all rights are reserved. To order handbooks, write Pritchett & Associates at 1315 Noel Road, Suite 1600, Dallas, TX 75240, or call (800) 992-5922.

"Peace of Mind for Pet Care" is used with permission of The Office of Planned Giving, Purdue University, West Lafayette, Indiana.

"Should an Accident Happen, What Can You Expect" is reprinted with permission from the 1996 edition of 'The Medic Alert Traveler' newsletter.

The author and publisher present this book with the intent to provide basic information and instructions, not to provide comprehensive information on each subject. For legal advice please consult with your attorney.

ATTENTION ASSOCIATIONS AND ORGANIZATIONS:
Quantity discounts available. Contact: Blazing Star Press. P.O. Box 89, Lafayette, IN 47902, (888) 237-STAR.

The Wishing Well

"A penny for your thoughts", she said.

"Umm, I might be over charging you", he said.

"Oh come on, Dad, tell me what's bothering you".

"Well Kitten, it's like this, while I'm in my right mind, I'd like to get it all recorded how I want thing done—if and when I might not be!"

"Do we have to talk about this today, Dad?"

"Yes, yes we do", he said. "I need to know now if my wishes will be carried out."

"OK, if it's that important to you, I'll help you, someone has written a book to assist with these decisions, we'll check it out".

It had become their custom to make a wish on important events.

"Want to make a wish on that?"

"Sure, let's do it!"

Together they crossed the park to the old wishing well. He reached into his pocket and pulled out a bright copper coin. They closed their eyes and made their wish and he tossed it down the shaft. They smiled when they heard its tiny splash.

Carol Suzanne

Contents

"Let your light so shine before men, that they may see your good work and give glory to your Father who is in heaven."

— Matthew 5:16(RSV)

Part 10 **Further Information**

Response Cards and Emergency Wallet Cards

Foreward

Elaine Todd has authored a unique book that assists its readers in getting some of life's most difficult and important homework over and done with for good. This book is a blessing for those of us full of good intentions, but in need of a helpful nudge at where and how to organize our personal, financial, and legal affairs. Inside the pages that follow, Elaine details a format and formula for assembling, organizing, and recording the myriad facts and figures that make up each person's unique and individual estate portrait. Along the way, Elaine shares inspiration, humor, and wisdom that make the task at hand pleasant and rewarding.

In twenty years of practicing family and estate planning law, I knew only one client who gathered her personal and financial affairs in the fashion advocated by this book. I served as executor of the estate of this particular lady, and her thoroughness and thoughtfulness in documenting her affairs made my duties clearly defined and a pleasure to fulfill. Not only did this client's efforts allow me to efficiently handle her probate estate, I was able to close the estate in record time and at a large savings to the heirs.

More typical of my clients was a kind-hearted woman who lived by herself in the village of Oak Park, Illinois—just west of Chicago. Miss Treny was a colorful character—a client of many years. She was prone to unscheduled office visits during which she often declared her sincere intentions of getting her affairs organized and in order. A fall on an escalator in a downtown Chicago department store at the ripe age of ninety kept this dear lady from ever returning again to her little apartment. Inside that silent, private sanctuary of hers, volumes of disorganized and unfinished paperwork greeted me when I assumed sole management of her affairs and ultimately served as executor of her estate.

For over a decade, Miss Treny had enjoyed playing the stock market with savings she accumulated as head of the typing pool for a large railroad. Though she played the stock market well, her holdings were spread almost randomly throughout various brokerage accounts, actual stock certificates she held personally, and in dividend reinvestment accounts maintained by individual companies. It was nearly impossible to nail down her exact holdings because there was no comprehensive list of her stock ownership in existence.

After months of dealing with the contents of her apartment in Oak Park, the time came when the unit had to be cleaned, vacated and surrendered back to the owner. At that juncture, I believed I had accounted for all items of real value in Miss Treny's estate. In order to meet the landlord's deadline to vacate, the few remaining odds and ends of furniture and household goods were promised to a local charity.

Although I hadn't intended to be present when the charity collected the last of the property, I wound up having to appear to give the movers access to the apartment. It turned out that my presence was warranted for that seemingly inauspicious event. When the movers picked up the bulky top mattress of Miss Treny's ancient old bed, a neat row of previously hidden parchment documents was revealed.

Between Miss Treny's mattress and box springs, she had stashed valuable bearer bonds—the equivalent of cash to whomever was in possession of them. Absolutely nothing in her scant recordkeeping even referred to the existence of the bonds. The bonds were not even referenced on recent itemized tax returns.

Despite all the hard work that those bonds represented, the proper disposition of them had been left entirely to chance. It made me wonder what else had been overlooked in the reams of paper and file folders that had already been discarded.

A thoughtful act has delivered this valuable self-help book into your hands. Make good use of the opportunity and the pages that follow.

Alan D. Schultz, J.D.
Delphi, Indiana, 1996

Alan D. Shultz, J.D., lives on a farm outside Delphi, Indiana, with his
wife, Deborah, and their three children. Besides practicing law, Alan
writes a weekly newspaper column and speaks to organizations on
such subjects as the importance of preserving family stories.

"This life is a test;
it is only a test.
If it were a real life,
you would receive instructions
on where to go and what to do."
— Unknown

Preface

Two years ago a dark cloud appeared to loom over my life and my career. Stagnation, boredom, and the moody blues had arrived for a long visit. Weeks and months of precious days melted away, while I continued going through the motions. I felt a desperate need to make some changes, to be stretched and challenged.

Thankfully, I discovered a creative writing class presented by a well-known local writer, Kathy Mayer. It was a new challenge, a welcome change. What a joy to begin to express myself on a deeper level and discover the rich rewards of writing exercises. The bonus was the wonderfully creative people who entered my life during this time, who became motivators and the support system that encouraged me to explore new ideas. They each represent an important puzzle piece of my life, forming a new me. A glorious light shines in me once again. I begin to understand that God has a plan for me. The challenge continues to be to learn the lessons He wants me to learn: faith, trust, patience, and perseverance.

I begin to appreciate and acknowledge the abundance of blessings and surprises that seem to be a part of my everyday life, but the biggest surprise is realizing that this book is a reality. When I reflect on how an idea for an entirely different project started almost two years ago and progressed to generating this book, I am amazed! You see, I had my own ideas about what people need and want. After all, I have spent thirteen years helping clients with money management, insurance, retirement planning, and estate planning! So, I developed a test product, conducted focus groups, and. . .

I was proven wrong! Imagine that? Blessings abound, however, because the wonderful participants in the focus groups very clearly stated what they DO want and would use. I honored their suggestions by doing more research for competitive products and realized they were on to something. A new idea was born.

All Together Now is a comprehensive method of passing on important information to family, friends, caregivers, executors, or trustees at a time when we can no longer take care of ourselves. It would not have been possible without the contributions of the many talented and generous people in my life.

THANKS AND PRAISE GO TO:

GOD, my C.E.O., who has guided and directed every part of this book from start to finish.

The many PARTICIPANTS OF THE FOCUS GROUPS in Lafayette and West Lafayette, Indiana, and Tavares, Florida, who were outspoken, honest, full of ideas, and generous with their comments about what they did and didn't like. They freely offered what they wanted and what they felt others would want. Thank you all for your contributions to the development of this book.

JANET L. MYERS, Dearborn Business Group, West Lafayette, my writing partner and business "Progress Partner." For your genuine support, your eagle eye for pertinent data, your encouragement and friendship, I'll be forever thankful and grateful.

KATHY MAYER, Writing and PR, Lafayette, for sharing her many talents and gifts, for encouragement, and for helping me to understand "honoring the process."

KATALINA MISKEY-GILP, my assistant, for getting me organized before either one of us realized the depth of this project and for helping me appreciate a different perspective. Her editing skill, suggestions, and friendship are treasures.

JULIE EMSWILLER, my office manager and right arm, for her patience during the transformation that took place during the writing of this book, for believing in me, for being a great listener as well as a friend, and for processing the pages of this book over and over again.

SHARON A. DEVANEY, PH.D., Consumer Sciences and Retailing, Purdue University, West Lafayette, for teaching me about focus groups and facilitating them for me, for being an informative advisor and research consultant, and for her enthusiasm and support.

ANITA NOBLE, interior design and BETH ELZER, cover design and illustrations. What a joy to work with women spiriting both talent and patience. True members of the "sisterhood."

CHARLES AND LEE FELLOW, my parents, for their love, encouragement, and belief in me.

ERNEST TODD, my husband, for his love, patience, and for always being there.

To my FAMILY many FRIENDS, CLIENTS, AND BUSINESS ASSOCIATES who have richly blessed my life, may God hold you in His tender loving care and bring you health, happiness, and prosperity.

SPECIAL THANKS to the many contributors of stores and articles, adding just the right personal touch to this book.

The Wishing Well, **Carol Suzanne**

Foreward, **Alan D. Shultz, J.D.**

Straight Talk:

> From a Daughter, **Janet Myers**
> From a Relative, **Sharon Quinn**
> From a Long-term Care Specialist, **Carol Sweek**
> From a Retiree, **Walter Mayer**
> From a a Sister, Anonymous

Should an Accident Happen... , **Bruce E. Jones**

For permission and approval of informational articles, many THANKS to **Medic Alert Saves Lives** and the **Organ and Tissue Donation Foundation**.

Elaine Todd

Introduction

I, Elaine Todd, do confess to being a clown. No, I'm not kidding!! A real clown with a painted face, long curly red hair, and bright colorful costumes, preferably in kelly green, purple, and yellow! My clown name is "Fannie." Fannie likes to face paint, but mostly she likes to tell stories . . . to just about anyone who will listen! She also likes to get the listeners involved by having each one add their very own special part to the story. That is great fun because you can never tell ahead of time how the story will end!

There is great joy and power in realizing that we can change the story to suit our own purpose or to have a "happy ending." We often forget that we have that same power to influence our own life story and that of our family as well.

Families of today are scattered across the country, usually visiting each other infrequently. Long-distance telephone calls help us keep up with the major events in each other's lives, but most of us probably have only a vague idea of the daily routines of our loved ones. The really important conversations and issues fall into the category of "we'll get around to it one of these days."

Our personal, financial, and legal affairs are certainly THE big issues that are rarely discussed. In the back of our minds, we know that an unexpected disability or death would leave our family with a time-consuming mess of paperwork, guesswork, and clean-up. How many of us have considered personally—much less talked to our family, about our preferences and wishes for healthcare, long-term care, or our funeral? Are our legal affairs in order? Do we have a current will, advance healthcare directive, power of attorney, and numerous other necessary documents? Are these important documents stored together in one place or scattered here and yon? WHERE DO WE START???

We start with your very own book, *All Together Now*. This book is all about YOU and will help you organize and record emergency information, important personal and financial data, personal preferences, and family history and stories for future generations.

"There are two kinds of people, those who finish what they start and so on..."
— Robert Byrne

All Together Now provides much-needed information, guidelines, and suggestions about emergency care, home care, long-term care, duties of an executor, and much more. You'll find a few short stories and quotes for information and amusement along the way.

Many of us are not yet ready to share confidential information regarding our assets at this point in time. *All Together Now* allows you to state your wishes, stay in charge, and to share personal, confidential information only when you're ready or only when it's necessary. A *letter of notification* is provided at the back of the book to send to those special people of your choice, to let them know you have completed the book and where it can be located in time of need.

Finishing this book will provide invaluable information and instruction for your spouse, children, or whomever you may designate as a caregiver during your lifetime or as an executor (administrator) at your death.

My hope is that in completing this book—YOUR book—you will discover the satisfaction of offering a tremendous gift to those you love and leave behind to pick up the pieces. I promise you, they will be forever grateful and respectful of your consideration of them.

Congratulations and God bless you for being willing to put together in this book the puzzle pieces of your life.

How to Use This Book

*A*LL TOGETHER NOW is **only** of value if you take time to fill it out. Yes, it will take some time, searching your memory banks, drawers, and files, but just think how long it would take for someone else to locate this information! At least you know where to begin.

It may be helpful to give yourself a time frame (for example, two weeks) to get it completed. **START NOW!** This will help you avoid procrastination. Remember, you're doing this for a very good reason—to help loved ones save money and precious time fulfilling your wishes.

• Use pencil on any sheet you may want to update (example: assets and financial statement). Extra pages are provided at the end of each section to add information or to make changes.

• It is important to date each sheet when you complete it. If you don't regularly update the information, at least you have provided a date of reference.

• When *ALL TOGETHER NOW* is completed to your satisfaction, MAIL the enclosed Notification Letters to at least two people you have chosen to handle your affairs, for example, executor, child, attorney, or sibling.

• Put *ALL TOGETHER NOW* in the location stated on the Notification Letter. Be sure to return it to that location when not in use.

Remember, this is **your** book. Write in it freely. Make notes in the margins, draw pictures, highlight, underline — have fun with it! There may be a section in the book that doesn't apply to your situation, so it may be helpful to make a notation that it is not applicable.

You'll notice that your book is designed to accommodate spouses or significant others (Personal Profile 1 and Personal Profile 2). However, some people may prefer to record information in separate books rather than combining the information.

Please take advantage of the Emergency Wallet Cards and the Organ and Tissue Donation Cards included in the back of your book. Tell your family that these cards are in your wallet.

A Response Card is also provided. Please take a moment to comment on what you liked about the book or make suggestions of changes or additions.

"Somebody has to do something, and it's just incredibly pathetic that it has to be us."

— Jerry Garcia

My goodness, Darlin,' you mean this is my very own book? I'm goin' to draw pictures and put stickers in mine! All that fillin' in the blanks is goin' to take some time—but even a clown can do it (I think)!

I do love my family, so I'll try real hard, because Lord knows they're goin' to need some instructions—big time!

I better get busy right now. Excuse me!

Love,

Fannie

Thank You, Dad!

Long before there were medical directives and other such papers, you talked easily about your desires whenever death approached.

My earliest memory of this conversation between you and me paralleled the death of a pet. I was probably 10 to 12 years old and, of course, you were 25 years older. Back then you said, "You wanted the curtain to go all the way down without hesitation when you died." You made your desires quite clear that you wanted nothing done that would cause you to linger.

So more than 45 years later, as your-end-here approached, I could stay focused on sharing with you. Because you had stated your desires in such a clear manner, you also had provided a common way of talking to the medical staff as we had among ourselves about your desires.

In that last week, you were always "in-charge of your curtain." In fact, we repeated that phrase to you during those last hours. It became our means to let you know that you had our permission for whatever speed you chose for your curtain's dropping.

The medical staff often commented how you never asked for pain medicine and how calm we were. You had made that possible.

Your absence is still a big loss. What helped in those first days after your departure was the solid knowledge that we had done what you desired. Thanks for your willingness to talk for decades about your desires and also for putting them in writing.

Miss you,

Your Loving Daughter

Charles Myers taught his daughter, Janet Myers,
the value of analogies and how they aid communication.
Now a professional speaker and author,
Janet shares with her audiences new analogies,
such as Lessons on Life and Business from Mother Nature.

Part 1

Personal
Medical Information

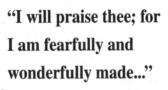

"I will praise thee; for
I am fearfully and
wonderfully made..."

— Psalm 139:14

One of my clown buddies fell in the parking lot of the hospital one evenin' after visitin' the children in pediatrics. Her clown companions quickly carried her into the emergency room to get assistance, but the ER staff thought it was a joke! They just laughed and laughed as the clowns got louder and more excited asking for help. It took several minutes to convince the doctor that they weren't kidding! That doctor just kept laughing as he treated my friend's arm.

Well, Ha, Ha! If I'd been there he would have gotten a smarty pinch—you know where—Ha, Ha!

Love,

Fannie

Emergency and Health Information 1

for _____ as of _____

Police, Fire, Ambulance
DIAL 9-1-1
or your local authorities

Police _____   Hospital Preference _____

Fire _____   Hospital Phone # _____

Ambulance _____   Medicare Card # _____

Clergy _____   Insurance I.D. Card # _____

I am a member of **Medic Alert**   Yes _____ No _____ (800) 432-5378
(See page 24)

I am an **Organ Donor**   Yes _____ No _____ (800) 355-SHARE
(See page 26)

I have a **Living Will**   Yes _____ No _____

I have chosen a

Power of Attorney for Healthcare   Yes _____ No _____
(See page 97-100, Important Documents)

IMPORTANT NOTE: *In event of my death, please refer to page 141, "When a Loved One Dies," for instructions and information.*

Health Information

Allergies

_____

_____

Healthcare Advisors

Primary Physician _____   Phone # _____

Address _____

Physician _____   Phone # _____

Address _____

Healthcare Advisors (con't)

Physician _____ Phone # _____

Address _____

Physician _____ Phone # _____

Address _____

Physician _____ Phone # _____

Address _____

Dentist _____ Phone # _____

Address _____

Eye Doctor _____ Phone # _____

Address _____

Pharmacy _____ Phone # _____

Address _____

Procedures

Surgery _____ Date _____

Physician _____

Surgery _____ Date _____

Physician _____

Surgery _____ Date _____

Physician _____

Surgery _____ Date _____

Physician _____

Surgery _____ Date _____

Physician _____

Surgery _____ Date _____

Physician _____

Medications

Prescription

Medication _____ Dosage _____

Physician _____ Date prescribed _____

Medication _____ Dosage _____

Physician _____ Date prescribed _____

Medication _____ Dosage _____

Physician _____ Date prescribed _____

Medication _____ Dosage _____

Physician _____ Date prescribed _____

Medication _____ Dosage _____

Physician _____ Date prescribed _____

Medication _____ Dosage _____

Physician _____ Date prescribed _____

Medication _____ Dosage _____

Physician _____ Date prescribed _____

Medication _____ Dosage _____

Physician _____ Date prescribed _____

Over-the-Counter Medications

Medication _____ Dosage _____

Medication _____ Dosage _____

Medication _____ Dosage _____

Medication _____ Dosage _____

Medication _____ Dosage _____

Medication _____ Dosage _____

Medication _____ Dosage _____

Alternative Medications, Herbs, Minerals, etc.

Name _____ Dosage _____

Name _____ Dosage _____

Name _____ Dosage _____

Name _____ Dosage _____

Name _____ Dosage _____

Insurance

Health Insurance _____ Agent Phone # _____

Health Insurance _____ Agent Phone # _____

Health Insurance _____ Agent Phone # _____

Life Insurance _____ Agent Phone # _____

Life Insurance _____ Agent Phone # _____

Life Insurance _____ Agent Phone # _____

Life Insurance _____ Agent Phone # _____

Long Term Care Insurance _____ Agent Phone # _____

Long Term Care Insurance _____ Agent Phone # _____

Auto Insurance _____ Agent Phone # _____

Auto Insurance _____ Agent Phone # _____

Umbrella Insurance _____ Agent Phone # _____

Homeowners Policy _____ Agent Phone # _____

Homeowners Policy _____ Agent Phone # _____

Date Prepared _____

Medical History 1

for _____

Personal History

Chronic/Ongoing Illnesses	Date of Onset	Treatment and Medication

Surgeries	Date	Outcome

Additional Information

_____

_____

_____

_____

Family History

Name	Relationship	Illness or Condition	Age of Onset	Age of Death
Ex. Mary Jones	Mother	Heart Disease	62	75

Date Prepared _____

Notes & Additions

Emergency and Health Information 2

for _____ as of _____

**Police, Fire, Ambulance
DIAL 9-1-1
or your local authorities**

Police _____   Hospital Preference _____

Fire _____   Hospital Phone # _____

Ambulance _____   Medicare Card # _____

Clergy _____   Insurance I.D. Card # _____

I am a member of **Medic Alert**   Yes _____ No _____ (800) 432-5378
  (See page 24)

I am an **Organ Donor**   Yes _____ No _____ (800) 355-SHARE
  (See page 26)

I have a **Living Will**   Yes _____ No _____

I have chosen a

Power of Attorney for Healthcare   Yes _____ No _____
  (See Page 101-104, Important Documents)

IMPORTANT NOTE: *In event of my death, please refer to page 141, "When a Loved One Dies," for instructions and information.*

Health Information

Allergies

_____

_____

Healthcare Advisors

Primary Physician _____   Phone # _____

  Address _____

Physician _____   Phone # _____

  Address _____

Healthcare Advisors (con't)

Physician _____ Phone # _____

Address _____

Physician _____ Phone # _____

Address _____

Physician _____ Phone # _____

Address _____

Dentist _____ Phone # _____

Address _____

Eye Doctor _____ Phone # _____

Address _____

Pharmacy _____ Phone # _____

Address _____

Procedures

Surgery _____ Date _____

Physician _____

Surgery _____ Date _____

Physician _____

Surgery _____ Date _____

Physician _____

Surgery _____ Date _____

Physician _____

Surgery _____ Date _____

Physician _____

Surgery _____ Date _____

Physician _____

Medications

Prescription

Medication _____ Dosage _____

Physician _____ Date prescribed _____

Medication _____ Dosage _____

Physician _____ Date prescribed _____

Medication _____ Dosage _____

Physician _____ Date prescribed _____

Medication _____ Dosage _____

Physician _____ Date prescribed _____

Medication _____ Dosage _____

Physician _____ Date prescribed _____

Medication _____ Dosage _____

Physician _____ Date prescribed _____

Medication _____ Dosage _____

Physician _____ Date prescribed _____

Medication _____ Dosage _____

Physician _____ Date prescribed _____

Over-the-Counter Medications

Medication _____ Dosage _____

Medication _____ Dosage _____

Medication _____ Dosage _____

Medication _____ Dosage _____

Medication _____ Dosage _____

Medication _____ Dosage _____

Medication _____ Dosage _____

Alternative Medications, Herbs, Minerals, etc.

Name _____ Dosage _____

Name _____ Dosage _____

Name _____ Dosage _____

Name _____ Dosage _____

Name _____ Dosage _____

Insurance

Health Insurance _____ Agent Phone # _____

Health Insurance _____ Agent Phone # _____

Health Insurance _____ Agent Phone # _____

Life Insurance _____ Agent Phone # _____

Life Insurance _____ Agent Phone # _____

Life Insurance _____ Agent Phone # _____

Life Insurance _____ Agent Phone # _____

Long Term Care Insurance _____ Agent Phone # _____

Long Term Care Insurance _____ Agent Phone # _____

Auto Insurance _____ Agent Phone # _____

Auto Insurance _____ Agent Phone # _____

Umbrella Insurance _____ Agent Phone # _____

Homeowners Policy _____ Agent Phone # _____

Homeowners Policy _____ Agent Phone # _____

Date Prepared _____

Medical History 2

for _____

Personal History

Chronic/Ongoing Illnesses	Date of Onset	Treatment and Medication
_____	_____	_____
_____	_____	_____
_____	_____	_____
_____	_____	_____

Surgeries	Date	Outcome
_____	_____	_____
_____	_____	_____
_____	_____	_____
_____	_____	_____

Additional Information

_____

_____

_____

_____

Family History

	Name	Relationship	Illness or Condition	Age of Onset	Age of Death
Ex.	Mary Jones	Mother	Heart Disease	62	75
	_____	_____	_____	____	____
	_____	_____	_____	____	____
	_____	_____	_____	____	____
	_____	_____	_____	____	____
	_____	_____	_____	____	____
	_____	_____	_____	____	____

Date Prepared _____

Notes & Additions

Should an Accident Happen,
What Can You Expect?

At any time, in any place, an accident can occur. Across the country, 80 to 90 million people are received in emergency departments each year. In about 20 million of these cases, treatment can be affected by some pre-existing medical condition, including epilepsy, allergies, and heart disease.

Any medical emergency can be unpredictable. According to one text:

> the emergency staff may have to treat an emergency victim without knowing the patient's name, age, medical condition(s), or what caused the emergency. Such situations, which are commonplace, may cause delays in diagnosis or treatment and can be fatal in serious life-threatening emergencies.

How does the hospital cope with this challenge? And what can potential patients do to improve their own chances of survival? Understanding the process is vital.

What to Expect

Assessment, intervention, and treatment actually will begin as soon as the emergency medical services (EMS) personnel—who, at this point, are usually paramedics and/or emergency medical technicians (EMTs)—reach the victim. Their first attention is to the "ABCs"—airway, breathing, circulation.

As Dr. Stephan G. Lynn explains in his book *Medical Emergency!*: "Before you are put in the ambulance, EMS personnel will conduct a physical exam and get your medical history so they can determine as accurately as possible what the problem might be." He notes that generally one EMT or paramedic will do hands-on assessment while the other records the "details of your medical history and your complaint." This includes verbal inquiries that test the patient's degree of awareness.

Dr. Lynn warns that this assessment, with its multiple questions, may result in individuals becoming impatient, but that it is in their best interests to "communicate as clearly and calmly" as possible and provide their physician's name, prior illnesses, allergies, and medications. Dr. Lynn identifies a core issue when he observes that "the patient has an obligation to inform, even though most patients don't." The reason they don't, he says, is because "they are so overwhelmed by the circumstances, it doesn't occur to them."

This interrogation is an important part of the life-saving process, and it typically will be done even for those patients who are wearing a MedicAlert emblem. However, even conscious patients may be confused and disoriented by pain and fear, and be unable to provide thorough replies. In addition, their condition and medications may be too complex to describe easily. For this reason, MedicAlert's professional education programs remind EMS professionals always to read the emblem's engraved information, regardless of their patient's mental state. This will help verify their initial assessment and identify any further complicating factors that require a call to MedicAlert's 24-hour Emergency Response Center.

The EMS team works with strictly defined "protocols," which guide them through complex cases by identifying appropriate levels of treatment. For example, the paramedic, who is qualified to perform more complex treatments than is an EMT, may hook up a portable electrocardiogram or start an IV to allow delivery of drugs, when needed. Paramedics are authorized to administer specific drugs orally or sublingually, by injection, through inhalation via mask, by intravenous lifeline, or down the breathing tube. According to one EMS handbook, paramedics can administer over 70 forms of drugs under these protocols.

The ambulance is connected by two-way radio with an emergency physician for securing instructions as needed, and, in essence, acts as a "pre-ER." (The radio allows EMS personnel on the road to alert the emergency room that a call to MedicAlert is needed.) Treatment on the way to the ER addresses the most apparent symptoms, with immediate attention given to life-threatening conditions, such as shock, severe bleeding, allergic reactions, and airway and respiration integrity. This stabilization acts to preserve vital signs and life-sustaining functions.

Upon Arrival

In the emergency room, the responding EMS team passes its findings verbally to the emergency department nurse or physician, who acts in a "triage" role to identify the most serious conditions. The field assessment is then reverified to determine the level of care needed.

This may well involve asking the same questions already raised by the first responders. Dr. Lynn urges patients to take advantage of this opportunity by "advocating for yourself"—ER staff work is a demanding and stressful environment where doctors "see patients as expeditiously as is possible, based on our assessment of the urgency of their medical condition." Thus, he says, individuals must "make certain that they clearly articulate their complaints and concerns." Bringing a MedicAlert emblem to the attention of ER staff can be part of self-advocacy.

After assessment, serious cases are sent directly into treatment, while a registrar will obtain from less critical patients name, address, and insurance information. They will then sit in a waiting room until the severity of their condition brings them to the top of the list. In some of the larger ERs, the minor cases are handled quickly in a special "fast-track" area on a first-come basis.

Following stabilization and treatment, the emergency medical staff determines patient disposition that can include laboratory and radiologic studies. They make a decision whether to treat now or to defer care and obtain specialty consultation. In serious cases, the emergency physician must decide to transfer the patient to surgery, a specialized facility, intensive care, or a regular hospital ward. One study indicates that about ten percent of all emergency visits result in hospital admission.

The Life-Saving Difference

But it is often those critical first few minutes of assessment and stabilization that can make the life-saving difference, and it is here that the MedicAlert emergency medical information system most directly comes to bear. The availability of concise information during the first seconds of an emergency can save the day!

For members of MedicAlert, the most effective treatment results from a three-way communication among the patient, the EMS personnel, and MedicAlert's Emergency Response Center. Especially when patients cannot speak for themselves, MedicAlert becomes their advocate.

For example, Stefen Weiss, a MedicAlert member with diabetes from Running Springs, California, reports that, in a recent crisis, he was in and out of consciousness and was unable to fully describe his medicine. He observed, "People in my situation with any type of chronic problem had best get it communicated to doctors." He continued, holding up his emblem, "And if they can't talk, this does."

Bruce E. Jones,
is manager of MedicAlert's
professional education program.

This article is based on "Savings Lives in Emergencies," a continuing education text for pharmacists published in coordination with MedicAlert by Zeneca Pharmaceuticals Group; and "Medical Emergency!" by Dr. Stephan G. Lynn with Pamela Weintraub, published in 1996 by Hearst Books. This useful text is written for lay persons and provides a full survey of emergency issues, including first aid and elderly/child care.

"There are two kinds of people:
Those who don't know and those
who don't know that they don't know."
— Unknown

Medic Alert Saves Lives

Your personal medical information is the first thing needed for treatment after an accident or emergency—it can save your life. You may be unconscious or too confused to give medical information. MedicAlert provides it for you. Unfortunately, most at-risk people are unprotected. Few are aware that wallet cards may never be found by first responders and store-bought bracelets provide little information. Only MedicAlert provides comprehensive protection. That's why nearly four million people in 46 countries are enrolled in MedicAlert.

MedicAlert's service starts with a wrist or neck emblem custom engraved with your critical medical facts and a 24-hour hot line number. Emergency responders read this information and begin work immediately. They can call MedicAlert's Emergency Center for medical details from your confidential computerized record including your medicines, allergies, physician, pharmacy, and family contacts. . . information that can help avoid life-threatening complications.

Eighty thousand lives have been saved since 1956, and nearly 250,000 members report that they received faster and better treatment as a result of MedicAlert. Enjoy the protection and peace of mind MedicAlert can provide. Call (800) 423-5378 today. It could save your life.

Peace of Mind When You Travel.
MedicAlert®
1-800-825-3785

Conditions, Allergies, and Medications Needing MedicAlert

Medical Conditions

Abnormal EKG
Adrenal Insufficiency
Alcoholism
Alzheimer's
Angina
Asthma
Bleeding Disorder
Cardiac Dysrhythmia
Cataracts
Clotting Disorder
Coronary Bypass Graft
Diabetes/Insulin Dependent

Diabetes/Non-Insulin Dependent
Eye Surgery
Glaucoma
Hearing Impaired
Heart Valve Prosthesis
Hemodialysis
Hemolytic Anemia
Hypertension
Hypoglycemia
Laryngectomy
Leukemia
Lymphomas

Malignant Hyperthermia
Memory Impaired
Myasthenia Gravis
Pacemaker
Renal Failure
Seizure Disorder
Sickle Cell Anemia
Sistus Inversus
Stroke
Vision Impaired
No Known Medical Conditions

Allergies

Aspirin
Barbiturates
Codeine
Demerol
Horse Serum

Insect Stings
Latex
Lidocaine
Morphine
Novocaine

Penicillin
Sulfa
Tetracycline
X-ray Dyes
No Known Allergies

Medications

Antianginal (specify)
Antiarrhythmic (specify)
Anticoagulant

Anticonvulsant
Antihistamine, regular use
Beta Blocker

Steroid
Chemotherapy Agent
Immunosuppressant

Special Needs

Blood Type (specify)
Advance Directive for Health Care

Organ Donor
Living Will

While the above are very important, any condition requiring continuing physician care should be identified in an emergency.

**"For God did not give us
a spirit of timidity, but
a spirit of power, of love
and of self-discipline."**

— II Timothy 1:7 (NIV)

Organ and Tissue Donation

O rgan and tissue donation and transplantation are subjects we don't often talk about, but considering the positive impact donation can have on another person's life, we should be shouting!

Approximately 25 different organs and tissues can be transplanted. Those in highest demand are:

heart	**kidneys**	**lung**	**bone and cartilage**
liver	**pancreas**	**skin**	**corneas**

Imagine being blind and then being able to see again because of a generous gift! Imagine leading the uncomfortable and restrictive life of someone on a kidney dialysis machine and being set free! Thousands of people could be helped if only more organs and tissues were available.

Everyone should consider themselves a potential donor. One person can help up to 50 people!

Becoming a Donor Is an Easy Two Step Process.

1. Decide to become a donor. Talk to your family, friends and perhaps a member of the clergy. Fill out the Uniform Donor Card in the back of this book. Be sure to sign your name in the presence of two witnesses, then have them sign. Family members are preferred witnesses.

2. Tell your family. You *must* let your family know your wishes as they *will* have the final say at your death. And sharing your decision with your family now will help them carry out your decision later. Carrying out your wish to save other lives can provide your family with great comfort in their time of grief.

For a free brochure on donation and
how to talk to your family about this important decision,
Call (800) 355-SHARE

Part 2

Personal Profile

"We don't see things as they are, we see things as we are."

— Anais Nin

My favorite graduation ceremony
was from Smiles Unlimited
Clown School on November 17,
1994. We were commissioned as
"official" clowns, complete with
new faces and costumes! We gave
roses, balloons and kisses to
family and friends.
What great fun!

Love,

Fannie

Personal Profile 1

for _____

Social Security # _____

Address _____

_____

Place of Birth _____ Date of Birth _____

Citizen of _____ Date _____

Parents

Father's Name _____ Date of Birth _____

   Stepfather's Name _____ Date of Birth _____

Mother's Maiden Name _____ Date of Birth _____

   Stepmother's Name _____ Date of Birth _____

Marital Status

Married _____ Divorced _____ Widowed _____ Never Married _____

Spouse's Name _____

Date of Marriage _____

Previous Spouse(s) (1) _____ (2) _____

   Date of Marriage (1) _____ (2) _____

   Date of Divorce (1) _____ (2) _____

Children

Name _____ DOB _____

Address _____

Home phone # _____ Work phone # _____

Spouse _____ # of Children _____

Name _____ DOB _____

Address _____

Home phone # _____ Work phone # _____

Spouse _____ # of Children _____

Children (con't)

Name _____ DOB _____

Address _____

Home phone # _____ Work phone # _____

Spouse _____ # of Children _____

Name _____ DOB _____

Address _____

Home phone # _____ Work phone # _____

Spouse _____ # of Children _____

Name _____ DOB _____

Address _____

Home phone # _____ Work phone # _____

Spouse _____ # of Children _____

Grandchildren

Name _____ DOB _____

Address _____

Home phone # _____ Work phone # _____

Spouse _____ # of Children _____

Name _____ DOB _____

Address _____

Home phone # _____ Work phone # _____

Spouse _____ # of Children _____

Name _____ DOB _____

Address _____

Home phone # _____ Work phone # _____

Spouse _____ # of Children _____

Name _____ DOB _____

Address _____

Home phone # _____ Work phone # _____

Spouse _____ # of Children _____

Name _____ DOB _____

Address _____

Home phone # _____ Work phone # _____

Spouse _____ # of Children _____

Name _____ DOB _____

Address _____

Home phone # _____ Work phone # _____

Spouse _____ # of Children _____

Name _____ DOB _____

Address _____

Home phone # _____ Work phone # _____

Spouse _____ # of Children _____

Name _____ DOB _____

Address _____

Home phone # _____ Work phone # _____

Spouse _____ # of Children _____

Name _____ DOB _____

Address _____

Home phone # _____ Work phone # _____

Spouse _____ # of Children _____

Name _____ DOB _____

Address _____

Home phone # _____ Work phone # _____

Spouse _____ # of Children _____

Name _____ DOB _____

Address _____

Home phone # _____ Work phone # _____

Spouse _____ # of Children _____

Great-Grandchildren

Name _____ DOB _____

Address _____

Home phone # _____ Work phone # _____

Spouse _____ # of Children _____

Name _____ DOB _____

Address _____

Home phone # _____ Work phone # _____

Spouse _____ # of Children _____

Name _____ DOB _____

Address _____

Home phone # _____ Work phone # _____

Spouse _____ # of Children _____

Name _____ DOB _____

Address _____

Home phone # _____ Work phone # _____

Spouse _____ # of Children _____

Name _____ DOB _____

Address _____

Home phone # _____ Work phone # _____

Spouse _____ # of Children _____

Name _____ DOB _____

Address _____

Home phone # _____ Work phone # _____

Spouse _____ # of Children _____

Brothers and Sisters

Name _____ Date of Birth _____

   Living _____   Deceased _____

Address _____

Spouse _____   Living _____   Deceased _____

Children _____

Name _____ Date of Birth _____

   Living _____   Deceased _____

Address _____

Spouse _____   Living _____   Deceased _____

Children _____

Name _____ Date of Birth _____

   Living _____   Deceased _____

Address _____

Spouse _____   Living _____   Deceased _____

Children _____

Name _____ Date of Birth _____

   Living _____   Deceased _____

Address _____

Spouse _____   Living _____   Deceased _____

Children _____

Name _____ Date of Birth _____

   Living _____   Deceased _____

Address _____

Spouse _____   Living _____   Deceased _____

Children _____

Name _____ Date of Birth _____

   Living _____   Deceased _____

Address _____

Spouse _____   Living _____   Deceased _____

Children _____

Other Next of Kin

Name _____ Date of Birth _____

   Living _____ Deceased _____ Relationship _____

Address _____

Spouse _____ Living _____ Deceased _____

Children _____

Name _____ Date of Birth _____

   Living _____ Deceased _____ Relationship _____

Address _____

Spouse _____ Living _____ Deceased _____

Children _____

Name _____ Date of Birth _____

   Living _____ Deceased _____ Relationship _____

Address _____

Spouse _____ Living _____ Deceased _____

Children _____

Name _____ Date of Birth _____

   Living _____ Deceased _____ Relationship _____

Address _____

Spouse _____ Living _____ Deceased _____

Children _____

Friends and Neighbors

Friend _____ Home Phone # _____

Friend _____ Home Phone # _____

Friend _____ Home Phone # _____

Neighbor _____ Home Phone # _____

Neighbor _____ Home Phone # _____

Professional Advisors

Executor _____ Phone # _____

Address _____

Guardian (Self-Appointed) _____ Phone # _____

Address _____

Attorney _____ Phone # _____

Address _____

Banker _____ Phone # _____

Address _____

Accountant _____ Phone # _____

Address _____

Insurance Agent _____ Phone # _____

(Life & Health) Address _____

Insurance Agent _____ Phone # _____

(Homeowners, Auto) Address _____

Education

High School _____

Colleges _____

Trade Schools _____

Additional Education _____

Personal and Business Affiliations

Church Affiliation _____

_____

_____

Service, Social, Fraternal, and Union Memberships _____

_____

_____

Special Awards/Recognition _____

_____

Hobbies, Interests & Activities _____

_____

Military Service: Branch _____ Service _____

Rank _____ War/Conflict _____

Enlisted ____/____/____ Discharged ____/____/____

Additional Military Information _____

Employment History

Begin with most recent or current employment.

1. COMPANY NAME _____

    Address _____

    _____

    Phone # _____

    Date of Hire _____   Termination Date _____

    Retirement Benefits: Yes _____   No _____

        Life Insurance Amount _____

        Pension Due: Lump Sum _____

                Monthly Income _____

2. COMPANY NAME _____

    Address _____

    _____

    Phone # _____

    Date of Hire _____   Termination Date _____

    Retirement Benefits: Yes _____   No _____

        Life Insurance Amount _____

        Pension Due: Lump Sum _____

                Monthly Income _____

3. COMPANY NAME _____

    Address _____

    _____

    Phone # _____

    Date of Hire _____   Termination Date _____

    Retirement Benefits: Yes _____   No _____

        Life Insurance Amount _____

        Pension Due: Lump Sum _____

                Monthly Income _____

4. COMPANY NAME _____

    Address _____

    _____

    Phone # _____

    Date of Hire _____ Termination Date _____

    Retirement Benefits: Yes _____ No _____

        Life Insurance Amount _____

        Pension Due: Lump Sum _____

                    Monthly Income _____

5. COMPANY NAME _____

    Address _____

    _____

    Phone # _____

    Date of Hire _____ Termination Date _____

    Retirement Benefits: Yes _____ No _____

        Life Insurance Amount _____

        Pension Due: Lump Sum _____

                    Monthly Income _____

6. COMPANY NAME _____

    Address _____

    _____

    Phone # _____

    Date of Hire _____ Termination Date _____

    Retirement Benefits: Yes _____ No _____

        Life Insurance Amount _____

        Pension Due: Lump Sum _____

                    Monthly Income _____

7. COMPANY NAME _____

Address _____

_____

Phone # _____

Date of Hire _____ Termination Date _____

Retirement Benefits: Yes _____ No _____

    Life Insurance Amount _____

    Pension Due: Lump Sum _____

                Monthly Income _____

Retirement Information

Retirement date   _____

Benefits began:

    Pension   _____

    Social Security _____

    Other   _____

"You think you understand the situation, but what you don't understand is that the situation just changed."

— Unknown

Comments and reflections on my working years:

_____

_____

_____

_____

_____

_____

_____

_____

_____

_____

_____

_____

_____

_____

_____

Date Prepared _____

Notes & Additions

Notes & Additions

Personal Profile 2

for _____

Social Security # _____

Address _____

_____

Place of Birth _____ Date of Birth _____

Citizen of _____ Date _____

Parents

Father's Name _____ Date of Birth _____

   Stepfather's Name _____ Date of Birth _____

Mother's Maiden Name _____ Date of Birth _____

   Stepmother's Name _____ Date of Birth _____

Marital Status

  Married _____   Divorced _____   Widowed _____   Never Married _____

Spouse's Name _____

Date of Marriage _____

Previous Spouse(s)   (1) _____   (2) _____

   Date of Marriage   (1) _____   (2) _____

   Date of Divorce   (1) _____   (2) _____

Children

Name _____ DOB _____

Address _____

Home phone # _____ Work phone # _____

Spouse _____ # of Children _____

Name _____ DOB _____

Address _____

Home phone # _____ Work phone # _____

Spouse _____ # of Children _____

Children (con't)

Name _____ DOB _____

Address _____

Home phone # _____ Work phone # _____

Spouse _____ # of Children _____

Name _____ DOB _____

Address _____

Home phone # _____ Work phone # _____

Spouse _____ # of Children _____

Name _____ DOB _____

Address _____

Home phone # _____ Work phone # _____

Spouse _____ # of Children _____

Grandchildren

Name _____ DOB _____

Address _____

Home phone # _____ Work phone # _____

Spouse _____ # of Children _____

Name _____ DOB _____

Address _____

Home phone # _____ Work phone # _____

Spouse _____ # of Children _____

Name _____ DOB _____

Address _____

Home phone # _____ Work phone # _____

Spouse _____ # of Children _____

Name _____ DOB _____

Address _____

Home phone # _____ Work phone # _____

Spouse _____ # of Children _____

Name _____ DOB _____

Address _____

Home phone # _____ Work phone # _____

Spouse _____ # of Children _____

Name _____ DOB _____

Address _____

Home phone # _____ Work phone # _____

Spouse _____ # of Children _____

Name _____ DOB _____

Address _____

Home phone # _____ Work phone # _____

Spouse _____ # of Children _____

Name _____ DOB _____

Address _____

Home phone # _____ Work phone # _____

Spouse _____ # of Children _____

Name _____ DOB _____

Address _____

Home phone # _____ Work phone # _____

Spouse _____ # of Children _____

Name _____ DOB _____

Address _____

Home phone # _____ Work phone # _____

Spouse _____ # of Children _____

Name _____ DOB _____

Address _____

Home phone # _____ Work phone # _____

Spouse _____ # of Children _____

Great-Grandchildren

Name _____ DOB _____

Address _____

Home phone # _____ Work phone # _____

Spouse _____ # of Children _____

Name _____ DOB _____

Address _____

Home phone # _____ Work phone # _____

Spouse _____ # of Children _____

Name _____ DOB _____

Address _____

Home phone # _____ Work phone # _____

Spouse _____ # of Children _____

Name _____ DOB _____

Address _____

Home phone # _____ Work phone # _____

Spouse _____ # of Children _____

Name _____ DOB _____

Address _____

Home phone # _____ Work phone # _____

Spouse _____ # of Children _____

Name _____ DOB _____

Address _____

Home phone # _____ Work phone # _____

Spouse _____ # of Children _____

"One life.
A little gleam of times
between two eternities;
no second chance for us
forever more."

— Thomas Carlyle

Brothers and Sisters

Name _____ Date of Birth _____

   Living _____   Deceased _____

Address _____

Spouse _____ Living _____   Deceased _____

Children _____

Name _____ Date of Birth _____

   Living _____   Deceased _____

Address _____

Spouse _____ Living _____   Deceased _____

Children _____

Name _____ Date of Birth _____

   Living _____   Deceased _____

Address _____

Spouse _____ Living _____   Deceased _____

Children _____

Name _____ Date of Birth _____

   Living _____   Deceased _____

Address _____

Spouse _____ Living _____   Deceased _____

Children _____

Name _____ Date of Birth _____

   Living _____   Deceased _____

Address _____

Spouse _____ Living _____   Deceased _____

Children _____

Name _____ Date of Birth _____

   Living _____   Deceased _____

Address _____

Spouse _____ Living _____   Deceased _____

Children _____

Other Next of Kin

Name _____ Date of Birth _____

   Living _____ Deceased _____ Relationship _____

Address _____

Spouse _____ Living _____ Deceased _____

Children _____

Name _____ Date of Birth _____

   Living _____ Deceased _____ Relationship _____

Address _____

Spouse _____ Living _____ Deceased _____

Children _____

Name _____ Date of Birth _____

   Living _____ Deceased _____ Relationship _____

Address _____

Spouse _____ Living _____ Deceased _____

Children _____

Name _____ Date of Birth _____

   Living _____ Deceased _____ Relationship _____

Address _____

Spouse _____ Living _____ Deceased _____

Children _____

Friends and Neighbors

Friend _____ Home Phone # _____

Friend _____ Home Phone # _____

Friend _____ Home Phone # _____

Neighbor _____ Home Phone # _____

Neighbor _____ Home Phone # _____

Professional Advisors

Executor _____ Phone # _____

Address _____

Guardian (Self-Appointed) _____ Phone # _____

Address _____

Attorney _____ Phone # _____

Address _____

Banker _____ Phone # _____

Address _____

Accountant _____ Phone # _____

Address _____

Insurance Agent _____ Phone # _____

(Life & Health) Address _____

Insurance Agent _____ Phone # _____

(Homeowners, Auto) Address _____

Education

High School _____

Colleges _____

Trade Schools _____

Additional Education _____

Personal and Business Affiliations

Church Affiliation _____

_____

_____

Service, Social, Fraternal and Union Memberships _____

_____

_____

Special Awards/Recognition _____

_____

Hobbies, Interests & Activities _____

_____

Military Service: Branch _____ Service _____

Rank _____ War/Conflict _____

Enlisted ___/___/_____ Discharged ___/___/_____

Additional Military Information _____

Employment History

Begin with most recent or current employment.

1. COMPANY NAME _____

    Address _____

    _____

    Phone # _____

    Date of Hire _____   Termination Date _____

    Retirement Benefits: Yes _____   No _____

        Life Insurance Amount _____

        Pension Due: Lump Sum _____

                Monthly Income _____

2. COMPANY NAME _____

    Address _____

    _____

    Phone # _____

    Date of Hire _____   Termination Date _____

    Retirement Benefits: Yes _____   No _____

        Life Insurance Amount _____

        Pension Due: Lump Sum _____

                Monthly Income _____

3. COMPANY NAME _____

    Address _____

    _____

    Phone # _____

    Date of Hire _____   Termination Date _____

    Retirement Benefits: Yes _____   No _____

        Life Insurance Amount _____

        Pension Due: Lump Sum _____

                Monthly Income _____

4. COMPANY NAME _____

    Address _____

    _____

    Phone # _____

    Date of Hire _____ Termination Date _____

    Retirement Benefits: Yes _____ No _____

        Life Insurance Amount _____

        Pension Due: Lump Sum _____

                      Monthly Income _____

5. COMPANY NAME _____

    Address _____

    _____

    Phone # _____

    Date of Hire _____ Termination Date _____

    Retirement Benefits: Yes _____ No _____

        Life Insurance Amount _____

        Pension Due: Lump Sum _____

                      Monthly Income _____

6. COMPANY NAME _____

    Address _____

    _____

    Phone # _____

    Date of Hire _____ Termination Date _____

    Retirement Benefits: Yes _____ No _____

        Life Insurance Amount _____

        Pension Due: Lump Sum _____

                      Monthly Income _____

7. COMPANY NAME _____

   Address _____

   _____

   Phone # _____

   Date of Hire _____ Termination Date _____

   Retirement Benefits: Yes _____   No _____

      Life Insurance Amount _____

      Pension Due: Lump Sum _____

                     Monthly Income _____

Retirement Information

   Retirement date   _____

   Benefits began:

      Pension   _____

      Social Security _____

      Other   _____

"It is through their work that most individuals write the story of their lives. They are both the author and the story's principal character. They are free to be the hero or the villain; success or failure."

— Malcolm Forbes

Comments and reflections on my working years:

_____

_____

_____

_____

_____

_____

_____

_____

_____

_____

_____

_____

_____

_____

Date Prepared _____

Notes & Additions

Notes & Additions

Part 3

Household Information

"The Lord is God and
He has given us light..."
— Psalm 118:27 (RSV)

Be sure my kitties, Cindy Lou,
Bunkie, and Fluff Puff get
plenty of hugs and tuna treats!

Don't forget to bring in the mail!

Love,

Fannie

Household Care

Pets

Type	Name	Food
_____	_____	_____
_____	_____	_____
_____	_____	_____

Veterinarian _____   Phone # _____

Address _____

SPECIAL INSTRUCTIONS _____

_____

_____

_____

IN CASE OF MY DEATH, MY PREFERENCE FOR THE PETS ARE: _____

_____

_____

NOTE: *Read about story on the Peace of Mind Program for Pet Care (page 57).*

Mail

Local Post Office _____   Phone # _____

Address _____

Security System

Emergency Contact _____

Emergency Phone # _____   Password _____

Garbage Pick-up

Name _____   Phone # _____

Address _____   Day of Service _____

Newspaper Delivery

Paper _____   Carrier _____   Phone # _____

Paper _____   Carrier _____   Phone # _____

Dry Cleaners

Name _____ Phone # _____

Address _____

Shoe Repair

Name _____ Phone # _____

Address _____

Magazine Subscriptions

Titles _____

_____

_____

Yard Care

Name _____ Phone # _____ Day of Service _____

Cleaning Service

Name _____ Phone # _____

Address _____ Day of Service _____

Plumber

Name _____ Phone # _____

Address _____

Heating/Air Conditioning

Name _____ Phone # _____

Address _____

Keys

Extra House Keys (Location) _____

Extra Car Keys (Location) _____

"The greatest thing in this world is
not so much where you stand as in
what direction you are going."
— Oliver Wendell Holmes

Date Prepared _____

Peace of Mind for Pet Care

Purdue University's School of Veterinary Medicine developed the Peace of Mind Program to address the needs of pet owners who want to provide for their companion animals in their wills. The program places an orphaned pet in a good, new home and covers the animal's necessary medical care costs. Program participants arrange estate gifts in their wills, which are used to pay for their pet's expenses.

The will provision must be significant, but it does not come to the School until the pet is in need of the program's services. Funding beyond what is required to cover the costs associated with the program supports related areas, including programs that enhance animal healthcare and improve our understanding of animal behavior and human-animal interactions. To maintain consistency in the program, the School asks participants to consider an amount of $25,000.

When an owner expesses interest in enrolling a pet in the program, the School provides suggested will provision language. The owner gives the School a copy of the will provision, the name of the pet, a brief description, and, if available, a photo.

Through the Peace of Mind Program, pet owners can rest assured that they have responsibly provided for their pet's future while also supporting studies and educational initiatives that target the needs of companion animals.

To my knowledge, there is no other pet care and placement program available at this time. I actually discovered it in an article printed in the Wall Street Journal sent to me by a friend. What joy to realize it's happening in my own backyard (sister city). For more information, contact The Development Office, School of Veterinary Medicine, Purdue University, 1240 Lynn Hall, Room 1177A, West Lafayette, IN, 47907-1240. Phone (765) 494-6304.

Notes & Additions

Part 4

Financial Information

"I will praise God's
name in song and glorify Him
with thanksgiving."

— Psalm 69:30(NIV)

I like stickers, so my bill payin' folder has birds all over it! That money just flies away!

Love,

Fannie ★

It Won't Happen to Me

Tom and Peg were in the prime of life, both in their early forties and successful in their careers. Tom, a C.P.A., naturally took care of the household and business financial affairs, while Peg worked a busy schedule at the hospital as a nurse. They had no children of their own, but Peg enjoyed attending to the many cuts and bruises of the neighborhood children.

Their busy schedules didn't allow much quality time together, so there was little discussion about money matters and the future. After all, there was plenty of time for that. They couldn't foresee that their lives were about to change forever.

On a Sunday evening, Tom suddenly became very ill. Peg reacted quickly, rushing him to the hospital, but Tom went into a coma. The diagnosis was encephalitis, and Peg quickly understood that Tom's life and future lay in God's hands.

Tom had severe brain damage, but after three weeks he began to make progress. After only six weeks, he was sent home, his mind like that of a child. Tom would never return to his business much less ever work again.

Peg knew she could take care of Tom—after all, caregiving is her profession, but that's where her confidence ended. Becoming the head of the household, making decisions, and handling financial affairs seemed overwhelming. She had no idea where to begin.

Sharon Quinn

Elaine Todd's sister-in-law, shares this story about a beloved cousin.

"There are three classes of people in the world: Those who make things happen, those who watch things happen and those who wonder what happened."
— Unknown

Monthly Income 1

for _____

	For Year 19_____
Salary	_____
Commissions	_____
Rental property	_____
Rental property	_____
Rental property	_____
Corporate profit-sharing	_____
Corporate pension	_____
Social Security	_____
Interest on savings	_____
Dividends on stocks	_____
Interest on bonds	_____
Annuity payments	_____
Insurance policy payments	_____
Veteran's benefits	_____
Part-time employment	_____
Business profits	_____
Royalties	_____
All other income	_____

TOTAL INCOME   _____

**"I started out with nothing.
I still have most of it."**

— Michael Davis
on the "Tonight Show"

Date Prepared _____

Monthly Income 2

for _____

	For Year 19_____
Salary	_____
Commissions	_____
Rental property	_____
Rental property	_____
Rental property	_____
Corporate profit-sharing	_____
Corporate pension	_____
Social Security	_____
Interest on savings	_____
Dividends on stocks	_____
Interest on bonds	_____
Annuity payments	_____
Insurance policy payments	_____
Veteran's benefits	_____
Part-time employment	_____
Business profits	_____
Royalties	_____
All other income	_____
TOTAL INCOME	_____

Date Prepared _____

IMPORTANT NOTE
to the person in the family who
pays the bills and records expenditures

The next three pages will be extremely helpful to the family member (or members) who suddenly faces the unknown in the event of your disability or death.

Be a dear, and take the time to complete them.

Total Monthly Expenses

Charitable Gifts

Tithe/Church _____

Other _____

Savings/Investing

Bank _____

Credit Union _____

Mutual Funds _____

Other _____

Housing

Mortgage (rent) _____

Insurance _____

Taxes _____

Electricity _____

Gas _____

Water/Sewer _____

Sanitation _____

Telephone _____

Maintenance _____

Cable TV _____

Security System _____

Other _____

Food

Grocery _____

Restaurant _____

Automobile(s)

Payments _____

Gas & Oil _____

Insurance _____

License Taxes _____

Maint./Repair/Replace _____

Cell Phone _____

Insurance

Life _____

Medical _____

Long-Term Care _____

Other _____

Entertainment & Recreation

Eating Out _____

Activities/Trips _____

Vacation _____

Other _____

Clothing _____

Medical Expenses

Doctor _____

Dentist _____

Drugs _____

Other _____

Miscellaneous

Toiletries, cosmetics _____

Beauty, barber _____

Laundry, cleaning _____

Allowances _____

Subscriptions _____

Gifts (special occasions) _____

Cash _____

Other _____

TOTAL EXPENSES _____

Date Prepared _____

Monthly and Periodic Bills

	Payable To:	Due Date:

Charitable Gifts

Tithe/Church _____ _____ ( )

Organization #1 _____ _____ ( )

Organization #2 _____ _____ ( )

Organization #3 _____ _____ ( )

Housing

Mortgage (rent) _____ _____ ( )

Electricity _____ _____ ( )

Gas _____ _____ ( )

Water/Sewer _____ _____ ( )

Sanitation _____ _____ ( )

Telephone _____ _____ ( )

Maintenance _____ _____ ( )

Cable TV _____ _____ ( )

Security System _____ _____ ( )

Housekeeper _____ _____ ( )

Other _____ _____ ( )

Automobile(s)

Payments (#1) _____ _____ ( )

Payments (#2) _____ _____ ( )

Maintenance _____ _____ ( )

Cell Phone _____ _____ ( )

License Taxes (#1) _____ _____ ( )

License Taxes (#2) _____ _____ ( )

Other _____ _____ ( )

	Payable To:	Due Date:

Debts

Credit Cards	_____	_____ ( )
	_____	_____ ( )
	_____	_____ ( )
	_____	_____ ( )
	_____	_____ ( )
Department Store Cards	_____	_____ ( )
	_____	_____ ( )
	_____	_____ ( )
Loans & Notes	_____	_____ ( )
Other	_____	_____ ( )

Childcare/School

Day Care	_____	_____ ( )
Tuition	_____	_____ ( )
Other	_____	_____ ( )

Taxes

Real Estate	_____	_____ ( )
Personal Property	_____	_____ ( )
Income	_____	_____ ( )

(m) monthly   *(p) periodic (quarterly, semiannual, annual)*

"The reason lightening doesn't strike twice in the same place is that the same place isn't there the second time."

— Willie Tyler

	Payable To:	Due Date:

Insurance

Homeowners _____ _____ ( )

Car _____ _____ ( )

Car _____ _____ ( )

Life _____ _____ ( )

Life _____ _____ ( )

Life _____ _____ ( )

Medical (#1) _____ _____ ( )

Medical (#2) _____ _____ ( )

Long-Term Care _____ _____ ( )

Long-Term Care _____ _____ ( )

Other _____ _____ ( )

Other _____ _____ ( )

Notes Payable

_____ _____ _____ ( )

_____ _____ _____ ( )

_____ _____ _____ ( )

Miscellaneous

Pharmacy _____ _____ ( )

Dental _____ _____ ( )

Other _____ _____ ( )

Other _____ _____ ( )

(m) monthly   *(p) periodic (quarterly, semiannual, annual)*

Date Prepared _____

Investments/Assets 1

for _____ as of _____

Certificates of Deposit	Location	Maturity	Ownership*
_____	_____	_____	_____
_____	_____	_____	_____
_____	_____	_____	_____
_____	_____	_____	_____
_____	_____	_____	_____
_____	_____	_____	_____
_____	_____	_____	_____
_____	_____	_____	_____

Bonds	Location	Maturity	Ownership*
_____	_____	_____	_____
_____	_____	_____	_____
_____	_____	_____	_____
_____	_____	_____	_____
_____	_____	_____	_____

Retirement Plans	Location	Maturity	Ownership*
401 (k)	_____	_____	_____
401 (k)	_____	_____	_____
IRA	_____	_____	_____
IRA	_____	_____	_____
Other	_____	_____	_____

Annuities	Location	Maturity	Ownership*
_____	_____	_____	_____
_____	_____	_____	_____
_____	_____	_____	_____

* See page 87 for definitions:
  T/C Tenancy in Common
  T/E Tenancy by Entireties
  JT/WROS Joint Tenancy with Right of Survivorship

Stocks

Broker _____ Phone # _____

Address _____

Broker _____ Phone # _____

Address _____

Company	Purchase Date	Number of Shares	Ownership*
_____	_____	_____	_____
_____	_____	_____	_____
_____	_____	_____	_____
_____	_____	_____	_____
_____	_____	_____	_____
_____	_____	_____	_____
_____	_____	_____	_____
_____	_____	_____	_____
_____	_____	_____	_____
_____	_____	_____	_____
_____	_____	_____	_____
_____	_____	_____	_____
_____	_____	_____	_____
_____	_____	_____	_____
_____	_____	_____	_____

Others (type)

_____

_____

_____

_____

* *T/C Tenancy in Common*
T/E Tenancy by Entireties
JT/WROS Joint Tenancy with Right of Survivorship

Real Estate

Location	Date Purchased	Title/Deed
_____	_____	_____
_____	_____	_____
_____	_____	_____
_____	_____	_____

Vehicles

Auto 1	Make _____	Model _____	Year _____
Auto 2	Make _____	Model _____	Year _____
Auto 3	Make _____	Model _____	Year _____
Truck	Make _____	Model _____	Year _____
Motorcycle	Make _____	Model _____	Year _____
Boat	Make _____	Model _____	Year _____
Riding Mower	Make _____	Model _____	Year _____
Recreational Vehicle	Make _____	Model _____	Year _____

Additional

_____

_____

_____

"When you count all your assets, you alway show a profit."

— Robert Quillen

Date Prepared _____

I told you that balloon company
stock would triple—Ha!

Love,

★
Fannie

Investments/Assets 2

for _____ as of _____

Certificates of Deposit   Location   Maturity   Ownership*

_____	_____	_____	_____
_____	_____	_____	_____
_____	_____	_____	_____
_____	_____	_____	_____
_____	_____	_____	_____
_____	_____	_____	_____
_____	_____	_____	_____
_____	_____	_____	_____

Bonds   Location   Maturity   Ownership*

_____	_____	_____	_____
_____	_____	_____	_____
_____	_____	_____	_____
_____	_____	_____	_____
_____	_____	_____	_____

Retirement Plans   Location   Maturity   Ownership*

401 (k)	_____	_____	_____
401 (k)	_____	_____	_____
IRA	_____	_____	_____
IRA	_____	_____	_____
Other	_____	_____	_____

Annuities   Location   Maturity   Ownership*

_____	_____	_____	_____
_____	_____	_____	_____
_____	_____	_____	_____

* *See page 87 for definitions:*
  T/C Tenancy in Common
  T/E Tenancy by Entireties
  JT/WROS Joint Tenancy with Right of Survivorship

Stocks

Broker _____ Phone # _____

Address _____

Broker _____ Phone # _____

Address _____

Company	Purchase Date	Number of Shares	Ownership*
_____	_____	_____	_____
_____	_____	_____	_____
_____	_____	_____	_____
_____	_____	_____	_____
_____	_____	_____	_____
_____	_____	_____	_____
_____	_____	_____	_____
_____	_____	_____	_____
_____	_____	_____	_____
_____	_____	_____	_____
_____	_____	_____	_____
_____	_____	_____	_____
_____	_____	_____	_____
_____	_____	_____	_____

Others (type)

_____

_____

_____

_____

* *T/C Tenancy in Common*
T/E Tenancy by Entireties
JT/WROS Joint Tenancy with Right of Survivorship

Real Estate

Location	Date Purchased	Title/Deed
_____	_____	_____
_____	_____	_____
_____	_____	_____
_____	_____	_____

Vehicles

Auto 1   Make _____   Model _____   Year _____

Auto 2   Make _____   Model _____   Year _____

Auto 3   Make _____   Model _____   Year _____

Truck   Make _____   Model _____   Year _____

Motorcycle   Make _____   Model _____   Year _____

Boat   Make _____   Model _____   Year _____

Riding Mower   Make _____   Model _____   Year _____

Recreational Vehicle   Make _____   Model _____   Year _____

Additional

_____

_____

_____

Date Prepared _____

Personal Financial Statement 1

for _____ as of _____

Assets (Ownership)

Cash on hand (Checking) _____

Cash on hand (Savings) _____

Certificates of Deposit _____

Money Market _____

Annuities _____

Government Securities _____

Mutual Funds _____

Stocks and Bonds (Current Value) _____

Accounts, Loans, and Notes Receivable _____

Retirement Plan (Current Retrievable Funds) _____

Business Ownership Interest _____

Real Estate _____

Autos/Boats _____

Life Insurance (Cash Value) _____

Household Furnishings and Personal Property _____

Other Assets _____ _____

TOTAL ASSETS _____

Liabilities (Debt)

Mortgages _____

Automobile 1 _____

Automobile 2 _____

Notes Payable to Banks _____

Accounts and Notes Payable to Others _____

Credit Card Balances _____

Insurance Premiums Due _____

Taxes Due _____

Business Debt _____

Other _____ _____

Other _____ _____

TOTAL LIABILITIES _____

Total Assets _____

Minus Liabilities _____

NET WORTH: _____

Additional notes on ownership or debt: _____

_____

_____

_____

_____

_____

_____

_____

_____

Date Prepared _____

Personal Financial Statement 2

for _____ as of _____

Assets (Ownership)

Cash on hand (Checking) _____

Cash on hand (Savings) _____

Certificates of Deposit _____

Money Market _____

Annuities _____

Government Securities _____

Mutual Funds _____

Stocks and Bonds (Current Value) _____

Accounts, Loans, and Notes Receivable _____

Retirement Plan (Current Retrievable Funds) _____

Business Ownership Interest _____

Real Estate _____

Autos/Boats _____

Life Insurance (Cash Value) _____

Household Furnishings and Personal Property _____

Other Assets _____ _____

TOTAL ASSETS _____

Liabilities (Debt)

Mortgages _____

Automobile 1 _____

Automobile 2 _____

Notes Payable to Banks _____

Accounts and Notes Payable to Others _____

Credit Card Balances _____

Insurance Premiums Due _____

Taxes Due _____

Business Debt _____

Other _____ _____

Other _____ _____

TOTAL LIABILITIES _____

Total Assets _____

Minus Liabilities _____

NET WORTH: _____

Additional notes on ownership or debt: _____

_____

_____

_____

_____

_____

_____

_____

_____

Date Prepared _____

Business Ownership 1

Business name _____

Address _____ Phone # _____

Date established _____ Date of ownership _____

Sole Proprietor _____ S-Corp. _____ C-Corp. _____

Professional Corp. _____ LLC _____ Partnership _____

Percentage owned by you _____%

By others:

_____ _____%

_____ _____%

_____ _____%

_____ _____%

	Yes	No

I have planned for the disposition of my business
in case of disability, death, or retirement. _____ _____

I have a BUY-SELL AGREEMENT _____ _____

Dated _____

Located _____

Funded by Insurance _____

Other _____

BUY-SELL AGREEMENT includes business
valuation formula. _____ _____

Business attorney _____

Address _____ Phone # _____

Business accountant _____

Address _____ Phone # _____

Contact person at the business _____

Date Prepared _____

Business Ownership 2

Business name _____

Address _____ Phone # _____

Date established _____ Date of ownership _____

Sole Proprietor _____ S-Corp. _____ C-Corp. _____

Professional Corp. _____ LLC _____ Partnership _____

Percentage owned by you _____%

By others:

_____ _____%

_____ _____%

_____ _____%

_____ _____%

	Yes	No
I have planned for the disposition of my business in case of disability, death, or retirement.	____	____
I have a BUY-SELL AGREEMENT	____	____

Dated _____

Located _____

Funded by Insurance _____

Other _____

BUY-SELL AGREEMENT includes business valuation formula.   ____   ____

Business attorney _____

Address _____ Phone # _____

Business accountant _____

Address _____ Phone # _____

Contact person at the business _____

Date Prepared _____

Definitions of Holding Title*

Community Property

Both real and personal **property earned or accumulated after marriage** through the efforts of either husband or wife living together in a **community property state.** Deceased spouse's will has control over one-half of community property. Community property state laws vary. There are eight community property states: Arizona, California, Idaho, Louisiana, Nevada, New Mexico, Texas, and Washington.

Custodian for a Minor

Under the **Uniform Gifts to Minors Act** or **Uniform Transfer to Minors Act,** an adult person can hold title to property for the benefit of a minor.

Joint Tenancy

Joint ownership of **equal shares by two or more persons with right of survivorship.** A person's last will has no effect upon such joint tenancy assets.

Life Estate

A **use of ownership in real property,** which terminates upon death of the life tenant.

Separate Property

Property owned by a husband or wife that is not community property; property acquired by either, **prior to marriage** or by **gift, will, inheritance,** or money damages for personal injury, and all of the rents, issues, and profits thereof.

Severalty

Ownership held by **one person only.** Person can be a natural person or a "legal" entity, such as a corporation.

Tenancy-by-the-Entirety

A joint tenancy between spouses with right of survivorship.

Tenancy in Common

Ownership by **two or more persons** who hold **undivided interests without right of survivorship.** Interests need not be equal, but a defined percentage of the whole will pass under the terms of the owner's will.

*Advice as to how to hold title to specific assets is the practice of law. These laws may vary from state to state. Consult with your attorney

Tenancy-in-Partnership

Method by which property is **owned by a partnership.** Specific interest in the property cannot be conveyed by one partner alone.

Trustee

The **Trustee** of a living or testamentary trust **holds legal title** to property for beneficiaries, who have equitable title.

"You belong to a small, select group of confused people."

— Message from a fortune cookie

Definitions of Documents and Trusts

Healthcare Documents

The **Advance Healthcare Directive** and **Healthcare Consent Act** combine the best features of a living will and healthcare power of attorney by allowing you to state healthcare preferences, and designate a person who will have authority to make healthcare decisions on your behalf. The advance directive gives you the right to control what medical treatment you will receive.

> The **revocation of Advance Healthcare Directive** is a document under which you may revoke an advance healthcare directive by declaring that the document will no longer be effective.

The **authorization for transfer of medical records** permits you to authorize the transfer of your medical records from a healthcare provider (e.g., a physician, nursing home, or hospital) to a new healthcare provider.

The **Healthcare Power of Attorney** allows a competent adult (a Declarant), prior to becoming unconscious or incompetent, to declare his or her intentions regarding life-sustaining procedures, and designate a person to make healthcare decisions on their behalf.

> The **revocation of Healthcare Power of Attorney** is a document under which you revoke a healthcare power of attorney by declaring that the document will no longer be effective.

The **Living Will** is a document under which a competent adult, prior to becoming unconscious or incompetent, declares his or her intentions regarding the withholding or withdrawal of life-sustaining procedures under certain circumstances.

> The **revocation of Living Will** is a document under which you revoke a living will by declaring that the document will no longer be effective.

The **Organ Donation Form** allows you to state your intent to make an "anatomical gift" of organs or tissues, specifies how the donated items should be used, and designates who will receive such items.

Personal Documents and Trusts

A **Charitable Lead Trust** pays income to charities for a term of years, after which the principal is paid to you or your designed beneficiaries. Although it can provide income tax benefits, its primary use is to substantially discount federal estate taxes and generation-skipping taxes.

A **Charitable Remainder Trust** is a tax-advantaged trust that allows you to provide income for yourself or someone else from assets that you designate for charity. You get an immediate income tax deduction for a gift to the trust, and you—and/or others you designate—receive income for life from the trust. Ultimately, the property goes to the charity. You can also avoid capital gains taxes and increase your income if appreciated, low-yielding property is used to fund the trust. The trust's assets are insulated from attack by creditors, and, in most case, avoid federal and state death taxes and probate.

The **Child Care Authorization** grants some other person (e.g., overnight babysitter) or institution (e.g., school field trip) temporary custody of a child.

If you are married and have assets of $600,000 or more, a **Credit Shelter Trust** plan can ensure that you and your spouse maximize the use of federal estate tax exemptions available to both of you. Upon the death of the first spouse, $600,000 is set aside in such a trust with the balance of the estate given to the surviving spouse outright or in trust. Assets in this trust provide benefits for the survivor but avoid estate taxes on the survivor's death. For example, on an estate of $1,200,000, this plan can avoid unnecessary estate taxes of more than $235,000.

A **General Power of Attorney** is a document under which a person (a Grantor) authorizes another person or entity (an Agent) to act on his or her behalf in a variety of financial and legal situations.

> The **revocation of Power of Attorney** enables the Grantor to revoke all prior power of attorney documents.

> In contrast to the general power of attorney, a **Special Power of Attorney** is a document under which a Grantor authorizes an Agent to act on his or her behalf in a specific situation only.

Guardianship/Conservator is an individual appointed by the court to guard and protect the property of someone who is incompetent to manage his or her personal or business affairs.

An **Individual Retirement Trust** is a self-directed IRA account, which tracks all IRA investments on one statement and is generally managed by a professional money management service. Your trust plan and its investments can be customized to maximize benefits available under the federal tax laws to minimize or eliminate income or estate taxes on the distribution of an IRA to beneficiaries.

The **Last Will and Testament** is the foundation of estate planning for most people. A will allows you to decide who will inherit property you own outright, appoint an executor for your estate, and name a legal guardian for minor children in the event both you and your spouse die. If you die without a will, these decisions will be determined by the courts or state law. If you are married, both you and your spouse should have separate wills. Wills should be reviewed periodically to be kept up-to-date with changing personal needs and tax laws.

A **Life Insurance Trust** is a type of irrevocable trust that receives proceeds of a life insurance policy in order to keep them out of your taxable estate. It can be important in providing immediate liquidity to your estate for taxes or your beneficiaries to avoid distress sales of closely held businesses or real estate. It can also provide significant long-term estate tax and generation-skipping tax savings for your children and grandchildren.

Minor's and Education Trusts are used to convey gifts of assets to children or grandchildren. You may give a minor child up to $10,000 a year ($20,000 if you are married), in trust, without filing a federal gift tax return or paying any gift taxes. Since the trust and/or the minor are generally in lower income tax brackets, income tax savings enhance overall savings for such purposes as education. Additionally, such trusts provide significantly more control of assets, flexibility, and tax benefits than do gifts to a uniform gift to minors account. Assets in such trust also avoid taxation in your estate.

Peace of Mind Program, developed by the School of Veterinary Medicine at Purdue University in West Lafayette, Indiana, is a program created to find foster homes for pets orphaned by the death of their owners. See page 57.

A **QTIP Trust** is generally used in conjunction with a credit shelter trust. Assets are given free of estate taxes to your surviving spouse, in trust, for the spouse's exclusive benefit. Upon death, assets included in the trust are taxable in the spouse's estate. The balance is delivered to your children as irrevocably designated by you in the trust. These trusts are particularly useful for individuals with children of a prior marriage.

The **revocable Living Trust** is a trust into which you place some or all of your assets. The terms of the trust can be changed or the trust can be revoked by you at any time. You can withdraw or add assets for any reason you choose. Because you have complete control over the trust and its assets, you are viewed as the owner for federal income tax and estate tax purposes. While you maintain control, you also achieve important benefits. The trust provides uninterrupted professional financial management of trust assets for you and avoids expensive, cumbersome guardianship proceedings if you are ill or incapacitated. A properly drawn revocable trust can also help you avoid unnecessary estate or inheritance taxes and generation-skipping taxes. Additionally, the assets in a revocable trust do not go through the delay, expense, red tape, and publicity of probate. A revocable trust provides for confidentiality and privacy. No one but the beneficiaries need know the terms of the trust, its assets, or beneficiaries. Trust resources are available to your family immediately after your death. These trusts can also be designed to address your specific family problems, such as minor children, handicapped, or spendthrift family members. Your spouse and children can be protected from unscrupulous persons by having the trust continue after your death until they are ready to manage the assets on their own.

Once you place assets into an **irrevocable Living Trust,** the terms cannot be altered and you cannot get the property back from the trust. These trusts are generally used to save federal and state income taxes or estate and inheritance taxes.

Notes & Additions

Notes & Additions

Part 5

Location of Documents

"O send out thy light and thy truth:
let them lead me..."

— Psalm 43 :3

I keep my important papers in a fire proof box. It has owl stickers on the outside because it's a wise thing to do—he, he!

Love,

Fannie

Important Documents 1

for _____

	Date Prepared or Last Update	Location
Healthcare Documents		
Living Will	_____	_____
Healthcare Power of Attorney	_____	_____
Organ Donation Form	_____	_____
Personal Documents		
Last Will and Testament	_____	_____
Living Trust (revocable)	_____	_____
General Power of Attorney	_____	_____
Special Power of Attorney	_____	_____
Birth Certificates	_____	_____
College Diplomas	_____	_____
Prenuptial Agreement	_____	_____
Marriage Licenses	_____	_____
Divorce Documents	_____	_____
Military Documents	_____	_____
Citizenship Papers	_____	_____
Passport	_____	_____
Vehicle Registration	_____	_____
Guardianship Papers	_____	_____
Litigation Pending	_____	_____
Prepaid Funeral Plan	_____	_____
Other _____	_____	_____
Other _____	_____	_____

NOTE: *For definitions of various documents and trusts, see pages 89 thru 92.*

	Date Prepared or Last Update	Location

Financial Documents

Bank Statements	_____	_____
Passbook for Savings	_____	_____
Pension Statements	_____	_____
Investment Statements	_____	_____
Income Tax Returns	_____	_____
Installment Payment Books	_____	_____
Credit Card Statements	_____	_____

Insurance Policies

Life
_____ _____
_____ _____
_____ _____
_____ _____

SPECIAL NOTE: *Accelerated benefits may be available on life insurance policies in the event of disability or terminal illness. Call the insurance company for details.*

Automobile
_____ _____
_____ _____
_____ _____

Misc. Vehicles
_____ _____
_____ _____
_____ _____
_____ _____

Homeowners _____ _____

Umbrella (liability) _____ _____

Health
_____ _____
_____ _____

"They laughed at Joan of Arc, but she went right ahead and built it. "

— Gracie Allen

	Date Prepared or Last Update	Location

Property Ownership

Deeds _____ _____

_____ _____

Mortgages _____ _____

_____ _____

Leases _____ _____

Vehicle Titles _____ _____

_____ _____

_____ _____

_____ _____

_____ _____

Safe-Deposit Box

Documents or articles that may be needed quickly when a loved one dies should NOT be kept in the safe-deposit box. (Examples: original will, burial instructions, cemetery deeds.)

It would be wise to get to know the laws of your state regarding accessibility to safe-deposit boxes at death. The box may be sealed by the bank at the date of death and accessed in the presence of a government representative for inventory purposes only!

If you are a business owner, please note that boxes leased in a corporate name do NOT get sealed upon the death of a corporate officer or director.

Ask your bank if they insure the contents of your box and, if so, to what limit. If the bank holds no responsibility, your homeowner's policy may offer coverage. If not, you may want to purchase supplemental insurance to cover valuable items.

Bank _____ Phone # _____

Address _____

Location of keys _____

Box Inventory _____

Bank Accounts

Authorized signatures on these accounts _____

Bank _____ Acct # _____

o Checking   o Savings

Address _____

Bank Accounts (con't)

Bank _____ Acct # _____

                                                               o Checking   o Savings

Address _____

Bank _____ Acct # _____

                                                               o Checking   o Savings

Address _____

Bank _____ Acct # _____

                                                               o Checking   o Savings

Address _____

Credit Cards

Major Credit Cards

Name _____ Account # _____

Name _____ Account # _____

Name _____ Account # _____

Name _____ Account # _____

Name _____ Account # _____

Name _____ Account # _____

Name _____ Account # _____

Department Stores

Name _____ Account # _____

Name _____ Account # _____

Name _____ Account # _____

Name _____ Account # _____

Name _____ Account # _____

Name _____ Account # _____

Name _____ Account # _____

Date Prepared _____

Important Documents 2

for _____

	Date Prepared or Last Update	Location
Healthcare Documents		
Living Will	_____	_____
Healthcare Power of Attorney	_____	_____
Organ Donation Form	_____	_____
Personal Documents		
Last Will and Testament	_____	_____
Living Trust (revocable)	_____	_____
General Power of Attorney	_____	_____
Special Power of Attorney	_____	_____
Birth Certificates	_____	_____
College Diplomas	_____	_____
Prenuptial Agreement	_____	_____
Marriage Licenses	_____	_____
Divorce Documents	_____	_____
Military Documents	_____	_____
Citizenship Papers	_____	_____
Passport	_____	_____
Vehicle Registration	_____	_____
Guardianship Papers	_____	_____
Litigation Pending	_____	_____
Prepaid Funeral Plan	_____	_____
Other _____	_____	_____
Other _____	_____	_____

NOTE: *For definitions of various documents and trusts, see pages 89 thru 92.*

| | Date Prepared or Last Update | Location |

Financial Documents

Bank Statements	_____	_____
Passbook for Savings	_____	_____
Pension Statements	_____	_____
Investment Statements	_____	_____
Income Tax Returns	_____	_____
Installment Payment Books	_____	_____
Credit Card Statements	_____	_____

Insurance Policies

Life

_____ _____

_____ _____

_____ _____

_____ _____

SPECIAL NOTE: *Accelerated benefits may be available on life insurance policies in the event of disability or terminal illness. Call the insurance company for details.*

Automobile

_____ _____

_____ _____

_____ _____

Misc. Vehicles

_____ _____

_____ _____

_____ _____

_____ _____

Homeowners _____ _____

Umbrella (liability) _____ _____

Health _____ _____

_____ _____

"Our chief want in life is somebody who will make us do what we can."

— Ralph Waldo Emerson

	Date Prepared or Last Update	Location

Property Ownership

Deeds _____ _____

_____ _____

Mortgages _____ _____

_____ _____

Leases _____ _____

Vehicle Titles _____ _____

_____ _____

_____ _____

_____ _____

_____ _____

_____ _____

Safe-Deposit Box

Documents or articles that may be needed quickly when a loved one dies should NOT be kept in the safe-deposit box. (Examples: original will, burial instructions, cemetery deeds.)

It would be wise to get to know the laws of your state regarding accessibility to safe-deposit boxes at death. The box may be sealed by the bank at the date of death and accessed in the presence of a government representative for inventory purposes only!

If you are a business owner, please note that boxes leased in a corporate name do NOT get sealed upon the death of a corporate officer or director.

Ask your bank if they insure the contents of your box and, if so, to what limit. If the bank holds no responsibility, your homeowner's policy may offer coverage. If not, you may want to purchase supplemental insurance to cover valuable items.

Bank _____ Phone # _____

Address _____

Location of keys _____

Box Inventory _____

Bank Accounts

Authorized signatures on these accounts _____

Bank _____ Acct # _____

o Checking   o Savings

Address _____

Bank Accounts (con't)

Bank _____   Acct # _____

                                                                o Checking   o Savings

Address _____

Bank _____   Acct # _____

                                                                 o Checking   o Savings

Address _____

Bank _____   Acct # _____

                                                                 o Checking   o Savings

Address _____

Credit Cards

Major Credit Cards

Name _____   Account # _____

Name _____   Account # _____

Name _____   Account # _____

Name _____   Account # _____

Name _____   Account # _____

Name _____   Account # _____

Name _____   Account # _____

Department Stores

Name _____   Account # _____

Name _____   Account # _____

Name _____   Account # _____

Name _____   Account # _____

Name _____   Account # _____

Name _____   Account # _____

Name _____   Account # _____

Date Prepared _____

Notes & Additions

Notes & Additions

Part 6

When a Loved One
Is Disabled

"Who through faith...
out of weakness were made strong..."

— Hebrews 11:33–34

I love visitn' the nursing home cause people's eyes light up when they see me comin' with ballons and hugs. We share some great stories, sometimes tears, but always lots of laughs!

Love,

Fannie ★

A Tragic Story

It is a glorious, sunny day in June, 1992, but Brian doesn't notice as he travels the country road to the cemetery in his small blue pick-up truck. Brian's mother has been gone for over two years now; his dad, almost a year. He misses them so much. The world seems a bitter place, and to make matters worse, his parents' estate is still not settled. The attorney seems to want to drag it out forever.

Suddenly, out of the corner of his eye, Brian realizes that a car is approaching the intersection much too fast—it's going to hit him!

Brian was in a coma for four months. When he finally opened his eyes, there was some hope of recovery, but three years later, the eyes continue to stare blankly. He cannot move, swallow, or communicate in any way. He requires 24-hour care in a nursing home, and the doctors say he may live like this for up to 30 years. Brian is not yet 50 years old.

The story continues. Brian's only immediate living relative is a daughter, Cindy, who he hasn't seen for 15 years. Cindy is in college many miles away, and is shocked to suddenly find herself the court-appointed guardian of her father—and of all his affairs. It doesn't take long for her to discover that there is also the matter of her grandparents' estate yet to settle. Cindy is picking up the pieces, and is overwhelmed! The story will continue for many years to come.

This tragedy may seem extreme, but unfortunately it did happen to a friend and client of mine. I began asking myself several questions, "How would my children know where to begin in case of my disability or death?" As the executor of my parents' estate, "Where do I begin?"

Elaine Todd

"We can do no great things—only small things with great love. "
— Mother Teresa

"The moment we find the reason
behind an emotion...
the wall we have built is breached,
and the positive memories
it has kept from us return too.
That is why it pays to ask
those painful questions.
The answers can set you free."

— Gloria Steinem

Health Information Resources

We find ourselves in a world of long-distance relationships and so often a family member is not available. Friends can often be depended on for at least short-term help, but then what? And who?

There are many local resources listed in the yellow pages of your telephone book. Outreach programs for in-home care are available from many retirement and nursing facilities, home healthcare agencies, hospitals, and senior citizen centers. Volunteers from churches provide support and services, such as meals, taxi service, housework, and administrative services (bill paying).

To locate human service agencies in your area, contact the county Area Agency on Aging. Another source is the Eldercare Locator (phone # (800) 677-1116), sponsored by the National Association of Area Agencies on Aging.

Other possible resources include:

Senior Centers (County office on Aging or
Area Agency on Aging can provide a
list for your area)

U.S. Department of Veteran's Affairs Check local listings, VA Office	Phone # (800) 829-4833
National Council on The Aging, Inc. 409 Third Street SW, Suite 200 Washington, DC 20024	Phone # (800) 424-9046
American Association of Homes and Services for the Aging 901 E Street NW, Suite 500 Washington, DC 20004-2037	Phone # (800) 783-2242
Nursing Home Information Center 1331 F Street NW Washington, DC 20004-1171	Phone # (800) 347-8800
Social Security Administration Office of Public Inquiries 6401 Security Blvd. Baltimore, MD 21235	24-hour Automated Service Phone # (800) 772-1213 Phone # (800) 965-1234

Alzheimer's Association   Phone # (800) 272-3900
Information Hotline

American Cancer Society   Phone # (800) 227-2345
Information Service

American Diabetes Association   Phone # (800) 232-3471
Patient Information Line

American Heart Association   Phone # (800) 242-8721
Information Service

Arthritis Foundation   Phone # (800) 283-7800
Information Service

Medicare   Phone # (800) 638-6833
Check local directory

National Hospice Organization   Phone # (800) 658-8898
Quick-Referral Hotline

National Stroke Association   Phone # (800) 787-6537
Information Service

Parkinson's Disease Foundation   Phone # (800) 457-6676
Information Service

Local Contacts

Name of Agency _____   Phone # _____
Address _____

Name of Agency _____   Phone # _____
Address _____

Name of Agency _____   Phone # _____
Address _____

Name of Agency _____   Phone # _____
Address _____

Name of Agency _____   Phone # _____
Address _____

Home Healthcare Instructions to Caregiver 1

for _____

Home Care Agency

Preference #1

Company Name _____

Address _____

Contact person _____ Phone # _____

This agency is my first choice because _____

_____

_____

_____

Preference #2

Company Name _____

Address _____

Contact person _____ Phone # _____

This agency is my first choice because _____

_____

_____

_____

_____

Additional Comments _____

_____

_____

_____

_____

"I do not know what your destiny will be; but one thing I know; The only ones among you who will be really happy are those who will have sought and found how to serve."

— Albert Schweitzer

Date Prepared _____

Notes & Additions

_____
_____
_____
_____
_____
_____
_____
_____
_____
_____
_____
_____
_____
_____
_____
_____
_____
_____
_____
_____
_____
_____
_____
_____
_____
_____
_____
_____

Home Healthcare Instructions to Caregiver 2

for _____

Home Care Agency

Preference #1

Company Name _____

Address _____

Contact person _____ Phone # _____

This agency is my first choice because _____

_____

_____

_____

Preference #2

Company Name _____

Address _____

Contact person _____ Phone # _____

This agency is my first choice because _____

_____

_____

_____

Additional Comments _____

_____

_____

_____

_____

Date Prepared _____

Notes & Additions

Questions to Ask Home Healthcare Providers

		Yes	No
1.	Is the service Medicare and Medicaid certified?	___	___
2.	Is the service licensed in your state of residence?	___	___
3.	Is the nursing service individualized to the client's specific needs?	___	___
4.	Are the employees of the service fully insured?	___	___
5.	Is billing processed by the provider (agency) to Medicare or third-party payers?	___	___
6.	Is there a charge for the initial assessment by a registered nurse?	___	___
7.	Is the client's care plan then coordinated with the attending physician?	___	___
8.	Is nursing provided on an hourly, a shift, or a 24-hour basis?	___	___

9. What problems or deficiencies were found in the home health agency last year?

_____

10. What services are available? *(Check all that apply)*

A. Skilled Care

		Yes	No
1.	Skilled nursing	___	___
2.	Care and supervision of catheters and drainage tubes	___	___
3.	Ostomy care and appliance changes	___	___
4.	Care of open or infected wounds or burns	___	___
5.	Intravenous therapy: pain control, chemotherapy, antibiotics, nutrition	___	___
6.	Supervision and instruction on self-injection	___	___
7.	Gastrostomy tube feedings	___	___
8.	Monitoring home ventilator program	___	___
9.	Physical therapy	___	___
10.	Speech therapy	___	___
11.	Other _____		

B. Home Health Aide

		Yes	No
1.	Bathing, shampooing, etc.	___	___
2.	Assistance with exercising	___	___
3.	Dressing changes	___	___
4.	Monitoring medication intake	___	___
5.	Monitoring blood pressure, pulse, temperature	___	___
6.	Meal preparation and light housekeeping	___	___
7.	Reporting problems to the nurse or doctor	___	___

	Yes	No
C. Other Possible Services		
1. Medical social services	___	___
2. Homemaker program	___	___
3. Companion program	___	___
4. Respite care	___	___
5. Helping hands for a new mother	___	___
6. Family helper program	___	___
7. High-risk pregnancy program	___	___
8. Home phototherapy for newborns	___	___
9. Portable x-ray services	___	___
10. Respiratory therapy	___	___
11. Medical supplies and equipment	___	___
12. Nutritional counseling	___	___

Many home Care agencies offer additional services. Do not hesitate to ask for a specific service or need. Some agencies specialize in specific types of care, while others offer a broad range of services.

How is Home Care paid for?

Private pay is always an option.

Medicare Part A of Medicare (the hospital insurance portion) will pay for home healthcare from a Medicare-certified agency if you meet the following criteria:

1. You must be homebound due to illness or injury.
2. Medicare services are approved by the doctor.
3. You need part-time or intermittent nursing care or physical therapy.
4. If you are receiving nursing care or physical therapy, then speech and occupational therapy, medical social services, and home health aides may also be covered.
5. Medicare does NOT cover:
   a. Full-time nursing care.
   b. Drugs.
   c. Homemaker help.
   d. Routine or custodial care.

Medicaid Benefits Medicaid is a welfare program that serves mostly the poor, elderly, disabled, and blind. Home healthcare may be provided as a less costly alternative to hospital or nursing home care. Contact your local county welfare department or Agency on Aging for more information.

Medicaid Waiver This waiver, approved by the Federal Health Care Financing Administration (HCFA) provides reimbursement for in-home and community-based services to Medicaid-eligible individuals. These services may include homemaker, respite care, case management, home-delivered meals, home modification or adaptive aids and devices, adult day care and transportation. For further information contact your local Agency on Aging.

Veterans Benefits The VA may reimburse for some treatments. For further information, contact the nearest Veterans Administration office.

Private Insurance Insurance benefits may be available from your group major medical plan with a short-term benefit. Home Healthcare insurance is available as part of a Long Term Care policy or as a separate policy and is currently being sold by many reputable insurance companies. Contact your insurance agent or the Insurance Commissioner in your state of residence for a list of companies selling long-term care and home care insurance.

It is NOT necessary to use the home health agency recommended by the hospital. Each person as a consumer has the right and responsibility to choose the agency that best suits their individual needs. By comparing prices and services of all agencies, you can make an *informed* decision.

Notes & Additions

Long-Term Care

We don't like to think about living in a long-term nursing facility, however, the fact is that we are living longer and the quality of life is not guaranteed. Families are scattered across the country, and in many cases both spouses are working, eliminating family members as caregivers. As a result, rehabilitation and long-term care facilities are growing in numbers across the country due to demand brought on by our aging population.

One national study* projects that 43% of those who turned age 65 in 1990 will enter a nursing facility at some time in their life. Among all people who live to age 65, about 1 in 3 will spend three months or more in a nursing facility; about 1 in 4 will spend one year or more; and only about 1 in 11 will spend five years or more in a nursing facility.

Long-term care is needed if, due to a disability or a prolonged illness, you can no longer take care of yourself. You may need help with activities of daily living, such as bathing and dressing. Sometimes more advanced care to help with feeding or assistance with toileting or incontinence is necessary. Long-term care can be provided by a family member, church support group, home healthcare agencies, agencies on aging, adult day care, assisted living facilities, or nursing homes and community care homes.

There are more women needing nursing care than men; 13% of women compared to 4% of men are projected to spend five or more years in a nursing facility. The risk, of course, also increases with age. To help determine your personal risk, you may ask yourself the following questions:

1. What is your current health status?
2. What is the average age of death of immediate family members? Did they live in a nursing facility during their lifetime? If so, for how long?

Costs for Long-term care range from $30,000 to $100,000 per year and continue to rise, increasing approximately 6% per year. Who pays for it? One way or another, we all do. Approximately one-half of all nursing home expenses are paid by state Medicaid (welfare) programs. To qualify for Medicaid, you must "spend down" to meet the federal poverty guidelines. Contact your state Medicaid office or Agency on Aging to get information on eligibility laws.

*Peter Kemper and Christopher M. Murtaugh. "Lifetime of Nursing Home Care," The New England Journal of Medicine 324, no. 9 (Feb. 28, 1991).

A common misconception is that Medicare and Medicare supplements will pay for Long-term care. In reality, Medicare pays ONLY for SOME skilled nursing care in an approved nursing home or your home. Skilled care criteria requires skilled medical personnel, such as registered nurses or professional therapists. The care must be available 24-hours a day, be ordered by a physician, and involve a treatment plan.

Many of us, about 49%, choose to pay for Long-term care out-of-pocket (our pocket or our children's pocket). As a result, many estates are rapidly dwindling. Children who are caring for a parent in the home have put careers on hold, putting their own lives and retirement in jeopardy. Often a family member is not available to be a caregiver due to differences in geographic location.

Increasingly popular is Long-term care insurance. It is not for everyone, however, if you have assets and sufficient income to pay the premium—without adjusting your budget—it is worth consideration. Long-term care insurance can provide you with peace of mind that you will have quality care, maintain independence, and not be a burden to your family.

Refer to page 129 which provides guidelines for choosing a long-term care policy. If shopping for a policy, work only with an insurance agent who is willing to help you fully understand the plan. It may be advisable to have other family members available for the presentation. In any case, do not allow yourself to be rushed to make a decision.

Adult day care centers are also becoming increasingly popular as a means to allow the caregiver to continue working outside the home or to have an occasional break from caregiving. Not all long-term care facilities offer adult day care; however, many facilities are constructing new additions to provide for this need.

Respite care is offered by most long-term care facilities on a "bed availability" basis. Respite care provides 24-hour care, usually for as little as two days up to two weeks, allowing the caregiver to take a much needed vacation or break.

Straight Talk from a Long-Term Care Specialist

All the Options

As marketing director of a long-term care facility, I am always looking for ways to assist and educate people before a nursing home placement becomes necessary or, in some cases, a crisis. I offer you some tips on what to expect should you or a loved one need a nursing home. Please keep in mind that nursing homes have changed a great deal over the years. Most homes offer special amenities that can actually enhance the overall quality of life for its residents.

Be aware of your options, exercise your rights, and make your own choices.

First, please, never promise a loved one that you will never "put them in a nursing home." One never knows what circumstances might cause you to have no other choice. Save yourself some grief because, believe me, they'll never let you forget that promise!

Second, check out your options. Always tour the facility before placement. Call ahead, or just drop in. Don't be afraid to ask questions. **Use the questionnaire in this book.** *Use all of your senses.* When entering the home, is it clean, odor-free, and pleasant to the eye? Is the staff warm and friendly? Do they offer to assist you? Are the residents well-groomed? Is the staff interacting with them? With you? For the most part, are the residents cheerful or engaged in some activity they are enjoying? Are the resident rooms clean, airy, and homey in appearance? Are there lounges, courtyards, dining areas, and recreation areas? Is there a chapel—and chances for continued spiritual growth? Are activities geared to the needs of the cognitive impaired as well as for the alert and oriented residents? *You might want to tour during mealtime.* Is the menu nutritious, well-prepared, and served? These are just some of the things you can observe on your own. Is the admissions coordinator well-versed about long-term care? Do they answer questions about your concerns in a self-assured manner? Are they looking out for the rights of the residents? Do they show pride in their position? Do they show pride in the facility? *Normally, your sixth sense won't lie to you . . . are YOU comfortable?*

Third, all persons entering a nursing home must have a family physician who is willing to follow their care into that home. Not all physicians do—be sure to check. Have you discussed the placement with the physician? What are the recommendations? What level of care does the physician feel is necessary for your loved one? There are three levels: *residential* or *assisted living* where minimum care is given—residents must be able to do most of their own care. *Skilled care,* the most acute type of care, may be covered by Medicare for a limited time. Skilled care includes treatments such as IV's, feeding tubes, therapies, ventilators, etc., that are prescribed by a physician. The most popular level of care is *intermediate* or *custodial* care. This covers a wide variety of illnesses; heart problems, stroke, cancer, various disabilities, Alzheimer's, Parkinson's, and senility, to name a few. Some residents in custodial care are very alert and oriented, while others may be mildly to very confused.

Lastly, after determining the type of care needed, locate the facility that best serves your loved one. You will find that some facilities offer all three levels of care, while others may offer skilled and intermediate, and still others, intermediate level only.

If the loved one is hospitalized, the social services department or discharge planners can assist you in calling nursing homes to check bed availability. Be sure to tour the facility. If the loved one is residing in his or her own home, with relatives, or in a residential setting, they must be pre-screened by a local council on aging before placement. This is especially true if they are already on Medicaid or anticipating the need of Medicaid (state funding) within the first year of placement. Remember, too, not all long-term care facilities are Medicaid-certified. If pre-admission screening (PAS) is needed before placement, the Agency on Aging will set up an appointment to do an assessment (interview) with the candidate to determine if nursing home care is valid. They will then send written notification to the candidate and/or family member and to the facility regarding acceptance or denial. During this process, prepare necessary paperwork, such a physician orders, a list of medications, a medical history, a physical, chest x-ray results (less than six months old), and any other vital medical information. Each facility has their own forms that must be filled out and signed by a physician. These are part of the state and federal laws that must be adhered to prior to admission into a nursing home.

Although not a prerequisite, at the present time, advance directives (documents such as powers of attorney, living wills, etc.) are something else to consider while waiting for the prescreening to be completed. You may wish to consult your personal attorney about these documents.

Remember, federal laws are pretty much the same for most of the US, however, state laws differ. If you or the loved one will be changing the state of residence, be prepared to wait for a longer period of time before actual placement due to additional paperwork.

Placement in a long-term care facility is not necessarily permanent. Many facilities allow short-term stays for 30 days or less for recuperation or rehabilitation care. Short-term care can also be of a respite nature for the caregiver at home. Sometimes a much-needed break or vacation for the caregiver can help them better cope with home care responsibilities. Adult day care, also offered by many facilities, allows a break for the home caregiver or to work outside the home. Again, this benefits both parties. Hours usually are offered between 7:30 a.m. to 7:30 p.m. and can be chosen to meet individual needs. Adult day care may be beneficial to those anticipating a full-time placement in the near future to allow the loved one to adjust to the daily routine and atmosphere of their new home.

Don't feel guilty about not caring for the loved one yourself. You are still caring for them—only through placement into a facility. Sometimes, it's the loving thing to do.

If you have any further questions, please feel free to call any reputable nursing facility, an agency governing aging, and, most certainly, your physician.

Carol Sweek

Carol has served the healthcare industry for over 20 years with love and compassion. In her spare time, she writes poetry.

"Live in harmony with another."

— Romans 12:16

Long-Term Care Terms and Policy Provisions

To help you better understand the language of a long-term care policy, several of the most commonly used terms and definitions are provided here. This list is not intended to provide comprehensive, detailed information. Be sure to carefully study a "specimen policy" before purchasing any long-term care or home care plan.

Long-Term Care facilities must meet the following criteria:
- Be licensed by the state
- Provide 24-hour nursing care (R.N., L.V.N, or L.P.N.) under the supervision of a physician
- Keep accurate daily medical records for each resident
- May be a free-standing facility or can be a part of another facility having a wing or unit set aside for long-term care.

Activities of Daily Living, basic bodily functions you must be able to perform to remain independent.
- eating (feeding)—ability to eat once nourishment is prepared
- dressing—ability to put on and take off clothing and necessary braces or artificial limbs, etc.
- toileting—ability to get to and from and on and off the toilet
- continence—maintaining bowel and bladder control
- transferring—ability to move in or out of a chair or bed
- bathing—ability to bathe

Cognitive Impairment is deterioration of intellectual capacity requiring 24-hour assistance to ensure your safety. A physician will use standardized tests to measure areas such as short-term or long-term memory loss, orientation as to person, place and time and abstract or deductive reasoning ability. Tests for dementia and Alzheimer's disease are common.

Daily Benefit is the maximum *amount* of money the long-term care policy will pay per day. Most policies offer choices from $40 to $200/day.

Benefit Period is the *length* of time the Daily Benefit will be paid. Choices range from one year to Lifetime coverage.

Elimination Period, sometimes referred to as waiting period or deductible, is the number of days you are confined in a facility before the policy benefits begin. Typical choices are 30, 60, 90 or 180 days.

Benefit Trigger is a term used to define when the policy takes affect. Usually this decision is based on medical necessity or the inability to perform a policy-designated number of activities of daily living (ADL). For example, most policies require an inability to perform 2 of 6 ADLs.

Waiver of Premium typically begins after 90 consecutive days in the nursing home and after satisfying the elimination period. Premiums will be waived thereafter as long as benefits are paid.

Inflation Protection is an important optional rider to nursing home policies. This rider increases the daily benefit of your policy by either simple or compound interest of 5% per year. This option is critical to keeping pace with inflationary increases of the cost of healthcare.

Home Healthcare Benefits are usually offered as an optional rider to nursing home policies to provide ongoing care in the home. HHC policies or riders are purchased much like the nursing home plan with options of daily benefit, benefit period, and elimination period.

Long-Term Care Insurance

Choosing a Policy

Long-term care policies are somewhat complex and usually difficult to compare. The following are basic coverages to look for:

- The policy should cover all levels of care:

Skilled	Assisted Living	Hospice Care
Intermediate	Custodial	Alzheimer's Disease, Senility, and Dementia

- No prior hospitalization should be required to trigger benefits.
- The policy should be guaranteed renewable, as long as premiums are paid.
- The pre-existing condition requirement should not exceed six months.
- Waiver of premium allows you to stop paying premium while collecting benefits.

The basic benefits you are purchasing are:

1. Daily Benefit (generally $40 to $150/day)
2. Elimination Period (how soon you want the benefit to start—generally 0 to 20 days)
3. Benefit Period (how long you want the policy to pay benefits—generally two years to lifetime)

Optional benefits include:

1. Inflation Rider can automatically increase the daily benefit amount by 5 to 10% per year, helping you keep pace with inflationary increases. Some states allow both a simple interest and a compound interest program.
2. Nonforfeiture Benefits returns part of the premium if you should choose to cancel your coverage.
3. Respite Care gives informal caregivers a rest.
4. Home Health Care includes nursing, aide services, therapy.
5. Adult Day Care
6. Therapeutic Devices

    Due to the difficulty in comparing a policy "apples to apples," choose the benefits that best suit your basic needs. Add options as your budget allows.

Choosing an Insurance Company

1. Choose a company with stability and financial strength.
2. Choose a company with top ratings from Standard & Poor (AAA), A.M. Best (A++), Moody's (Aaa), and Duff & Phelps (AAA).
3. Choose a company with a track record of paying claims.

Notes & Additions

_____

_____

_____

_____

_____

_____

_____

_____

_____

_____

_____

_____

_____

_____

_____

_____

_____

_____

_____

_____

_____

_____

_____

_____

_____

Long-Term Care Instructions to Caregiver 1

for _____

Rehabilitation/Long-Term Care Facility

Preference #1

Company Name _____

Address _____

Contact person _____ Phone # _____

This rehab/LTC facility is my first choice because _____

_____

_____

_____

Preference #2

Company Name _____

Address _____

Contact person _____ Phone # _____

This rehab/LTC facility is my second choice because _____

_____

_____

_____

Additional Comments _____

_____

_____

_____

_____

Date Prepared _____

Notes & Additions

Long-Term Care Instructions to Caregiver 2

for _____

Rehabilitation/Long-Term Care Facility

Preference #1

Company Name _____

Address _____

Contact person _____ Phone # _____

This rehab/LTC facility is my first choice because _____

_____

_____

_____

Preference #2

Company Name _____

Address _____

Contact person _____ Phone # _____

This rehab/LTC facility is my second choice because _____

_____

_____

_____

Additional Comments _____

_____

_____

_____

_____

Date Prepared _____

Notes & Additions

_____

_____

_____

_____

_____

_____

_____

_____

_____

_____

_____

_____

_____

_____

_____

_____

_____

_____

_____

_____

_____

_____

_____

_____

_____

Questions to Ask
Rehabilitation/Nursing Home Facility

	Yes	No
1. Is it a Medicare-Medicaid approved facility?	_____	_____
2. What is the history of state inspection reports? Serious violations?	_____	_____
3. Are current residents happy living here?	_____	_____
Talk to resident about housekeeping, food, and attitudes of caregiving employees.		
4. Are rights of privacy respected?	_____	_____
5. What is the employee/resident ratio?		
(4 to 1 is a good ratio) _____ to _____		
6. What levels of care do you provide?		
a. skilled nursing	_____	_____
b. custodial/intermediate	_____	_____
c. assisted living	_____	_____
d. Alzheimer's wing	_____	_____
e. adult day care	_____	_____
f. physical rehabilitation therapy	_____	_____
g. mental rehabilitation therapy	_____	_____
7. Is a deposit required?	_____	_____
a. Private room: cost/day _____		
b. Semiprivate room: cost/day _____		
8. Itemized statement detailing what is/is not included in daily rate?	_____	_____
9. Are there emergency procedures in place with adequate equipment, doctors, and ambulance available?	_____	_____
10. Are planned activities available?	_____	_____
a. Is there a recreation director on staff?	_____	_____
b. Is there an activities room available?	_____	_____
c. Is there a room for private family visits?	_____	_____
d. Is there an outdoor area available for resident use?	_____	_____
e. Is there a lounge for watching TV, reading, games, etc?	_____	_____

"People are generally better persuaded by the reasons which they have themselves discovered than by those which have come into the minds of others."

— Pascal

Notes & Additions

Part 7

When a Loved One Dies

"In my Father's house are many mansions. . .
And if I go and prepare a place for you,
I will come again and receive you unto myself;
that where I am, there ye may be also."

—John 14: 2–3

When I go to be with the Lord,
make sure I'm wearin' my green
satin vest with the sequined
balloons. He'll like how the
colors reflect the light!
Love,

Fannie ★

It's My Funeral

My wife and I decided to take a little of our "mad money" and invest in some real estate. "Might just come in handy in our old age," she said. So we snooped around for a while in the Kokomo-Burlington area but found it a tad salty for our taste. Finally, by sheer chance, we stumbled across exactly what we had been looking for, just a few miles east and south of Cutler, off a narrow gravel road. Some majestic cedar trees, plenty of water and grass, and a small monument marking where once stood a Methodist church founded back in the early 1800s. A few Methodists in the area, to boot. They don't talk a whole lot and keep pretty much to themselves. So the next day, we plunked down $70 each and bought ourselves two gravesites. Yes, sir, that's exactly what we did. Bought some real estate.

In short, we decided to start practicing what I had been preaching all these years: Plan for your funeral, and do it now! Don't dump it on the kids or your spouse. That's not fair. And I have a few other convictions that I will file away in our lock box tomorrow morning.

1. Don't bury me from a store! I was baptized, confirmed, married, and ordained inside God's church. So why would you disgrace me by hauling my carcass off to a business establishment? A mortuary is for selling goods and services, plus rental of a Cadillac hearse, if you like. (Sadly enough, 90 percent of the memorial services I conducted were in a store.) Don't blame the Christian morticians. They don't understand it either.

2. Dress me in my old pink sweater and those yellow slacks from Land's End. I hate suits, shirts, and neckties. This will be my last snub of sartorial arrogance. And please don't stick a Bible in my hand, just "Old Green," my 40-year-old Shakespeare rod and reel ("and I will make you to become fishers," etc. plus a few 5-pound walleyes).

3. A cloth-covered casket with a small placard on top designed by son Jim: "I'd rather be here than in a Cabinet meeting."

4. No blanket of baby roses from the grandkids, either. Just a Mason jar filled with dandelions, those feisty little symbols of the Resurrection.

5. I don't want my pastoral peers to sing that horrendous hymn composed by a weary bishop who obviously had grandiose ambitions of being a songwriter. Even God cannot sing that atrocity! Sing "Amazing Grace," "Shall We Gather at the River?" and "Jesus Loves Me." My son Dan will lead his musical group in "I'll Fly Away."

6.   And, in case I expire first, God forbid, Hezekiah Malone will preach the sermon. At the graveside, Clare McKinney will read Ecclesiastics 3:1–8 and release a pillowcase full of butterflies.

7.   My four sons will carry me to the grave. God knows I carried them long enough.

8.   No skinny slices of ham, scalloped potatoes, green beans, and orange Jello for the funeral dinner. Fried catfish or Cornish hens will do just fine. My friends deserve the best.

A Sinner Saved by Grace,

Walter

P.S. And since the place will be packed, RSVPs will be expected.

Walter Mayer is the retired Superintendent of the
South Bend, Indiana, District of the United Methodist Church.
He is a writer, a lover of life, nature and people. Most likely in that order.

Instructions

Person responsible for making final arrangements

Name _____

Address _____

_____

Phone # _____

ALTERNATE

Name _____

Address _____

_____

Phone # _____

1. A. Refer to page 34 or 46, **Professional Advisor,** to note named **Executor**.

   B. Refer to page 145 or 151 for the deceased's preferences for **Funeral and Burial Plans** and to page 147 or 153 for **Obituary Information.**

2. Contact a Funeral Director

   You may expect the following services from the funeral director:

   1. Arranging for the service, as requested

      a. Providing an itemized price list for casket, vault cremation, etc.

      b. Assisting in obtaining a burial plot, if necessary

   2. Submitting the Obituary Information to publications and newspapers of your choice.

   3. Providing Death Certificates; you will need several original copies.

   4. Explaining death benefits to the family for Social Security, veterans, etc.

   5. Filing claims for Social Security, life insurance, pension benefits, etc.

   6. Providing notification to employer, if necessary.

   7. Some funeral directors may also offer additional services, such as counseling on debt management, etc.

3. Notify and/or converse with the following special people in my life.
   They are to be treated with consideration on my behalf because I loved them dearly.

Name	Phone #	Relationship
_____	_____	_____
_____	_____	_____
_____	_____	_____
_____	_____	_____
_____	_____	_____

4. Locate important documents; see pages 97 or 101 of this book. File any claims or forms as soon as possible.

5. Notify the life insurance agent, listed on page 35 or 47 of this book.

6. Notify the employer (or if retired, previous employer) listed on page 36 or 48 of this book.
   A. Obtain information on benefits due and filing claims.
   B. Ask about pension fund benefits [profit sharing and 401(K)], accrued vacation and sick pay, disability income, terminal pay allowances, and credit or savings plan balances.
   C. Ask if dependents remain eligible for benefits and for how long.

7. Refer to legal responsibilities of executor on page 161 of this book.

8. Gather all current bills. Refer to monthly expenses on page 67 and **due** dates of monthly and periodic bills on pages 68 to 70 of this book.

9. Notify all Professional Advisors listed on pages 34 and 46 of this book

10. Contact Organizations on page 35 or 47, listed under Personal Business Affiliations.

Additional Information

_____

_____

_____

_____

_____

"I feel so bad since you've gone.
It's almost like having you here."

— Unknown

Types of Funeral Services Available

Traditional Service

Includes transfer of the deceased, embalming, preparation, afternoon-to-evening viewing, with the service the next day. Transfer to the cemetery with graveside service. Transfer of flowers. Filing for death certificates, veterans benefits, and Social Security benefits. Costs vary with the selection of casket, vault, and miscellaneous charges (open-closing of grave, honorariums for minister and organist, flowers for casket spray, death certificates).

Same-Day Service

Includes all of the above, except the viewing and service would occur on the same day. Requires casket and vault.

Graveside Service

No viewing or service at the funeral home. Service at cemetery only. Requires casket and vault.

Direct Burial

No services provided. Requires casket and vault.

Cremation with Service

Viewing and service same as either traditional or same-day service. Would require rental casket. Some cemeteries may require an urn vault. Open-closing approximately one-half the regular grave open-closing cost.

Cremation with Memorial Service

Service with urn at funeral home. Transfer of urn to graveside for service and burial. No casket required. Some cemeteries may require an urn vault.

Direct Cremation

No viewing or service. Cremains given to family. No casket or vault required.

Funeral and Burial Plans 1

for _____

Clergy or Person Officiating _____ Phone # _____

Funeral Home Preference _____ Phone # _____

Location of Service _____

Type of Service Preferred:

Traditional	_____	Cremation with Memorial Service	_____
Direct Burial	_____	Cremation with Service	_____
Same Day	_____	Direct Cremation	_____

_____ I have purchased a cemetery plot in _____

Cemetery Name _____

Address _____

Lot # _____ Block # _____ Section # _____

Location of Deed _____

Marker: Yes _____ No _____

_____ I have a prepaid funeral plan # _____

See location of Important Documents on pages 97 to 100 of this book.

Music: Organist Yes_____ No_____ Vocalist Yes_____ No_____

Selections _____

_____

_____

Viewing Wishes: Open Casket _____ Closed Casket _____

Special Requests (casket, poems/Bible passages, clothing, hairdresser, etc.)

_____

_____

_____

In lieu of flowers, please make contributions to _____

_____

Pallbearers

1. Name _____ Phone # _____

   Address _____

2. Name _____ Phone # _____

   Address _____

3. Name _____ Phone # _____

   Address _____

4. Name _____ Phone # _____

   Address _____

5. Name _____ Phone # _____

   Address _____

6. Name _____ Phone # _____

   Address _____

7. Name _____ Phone # _____

   Address _____

8. Name _____ Phone # _____

   Address _____

Obituary Information

Full Name _____

Date of Birth ____/____/____   Place of Birth _____

Spouse _____

Date & Place of Marriage _____

Spouse Survives: Yes _____ No _____   Date of Death ____/____/____

See page 35 for:

Education   Special Awards/Recognitions

Church Affiliation   Hobbies and Activities

Service, Social, Fraternal, and Union Memberships   Military Service

Survivors

	Name	City	State
Father			
Mother			
Sons			
Daughters			
Brothers			

Sisters _____

_____

_____

_____

Number of Grandchildren _____ Great-Grandchildren _____

See Personal Profile, pages 30 to 33 for names and addresses of siblings, grandchildren, and great-grandchildren.

Cemetery

_____

Newspapers, professional and alumni newsletters, magazines and
organizations to send copies of this obituary:

Name _____

Address _____

Name _____

Address _____

Name _____

Address _____

Name _____

Address _____

Additional Information

_____

_____

_____

_____

_____

Date Prepared _____

Notes & Additions

Funeral and Burial Plans 2

for _____

Clergy or Person Officiating _____ Phone # _____

Funeral Home Preference _____ Phone # _____

Location of Service _____

Type of Service Preferred:

Traditional	_____	Cremation with Memorial Service	_____
Direct Burial	_____	Cremation with Service	_____
Same Day	_____	Direct Cremation	_____

_____ I have purchased a cemetery plot in _____

Cemetery Name _____

Address _____

Lot # _____ Block # _____ Section # _____

Location of Deed _____

Marker: Yes _____ No _____

_____ I have a prepaid funeral plan # _____

See location of Important Documents on pages 101 to 104 of this book.

Music: Organist Yes_____ No_____ Vocalist Yes_____ No_____

Selections _____

_____

_____

Viewing Wishes: Open Casket _____ Closed Casket _____

Special Requests (casket, poems/Bible passages, clothing, hairdresser, etc.)

_____

_____

_____

In lieu of flowers, please make contributions to _____

_____

Pallbearers

1. Name _____ Phone # _____

   Address _____

2. Name _____ Phone # _____

   Address _____

3. Name _____ Phone # _____

   Address _____

4. Name _____ Phone # _____

   Address _____

5. Name _____ Phone # _____

   Address _____

6. Name _____ Phone # _____

   Address _____

7. Name _____ Phone # _____

   Address _____

8. Name _____ Phone # _____

   Address _____

Obituary Information

Full Name _____

Date of Birth _____/_____/_____   Place of Birth _____

Spouse _____

Date & Place of Marriage _____

Spouse Survives: Yes _____ No _____   Date of Death _____/_____/_____

See page 47 for:

    Education   Special Awards/Recognitions

    Church Affiliation   Hobbies and Activities

    Service, Social, Fraternal, and Union Memberships   Military Service

Survivors

	Name	City	State
Father			
Mother			
Sons			
Daughters			
Brothers			

Sisters   _____

_____

_____

_____

Number of Grandchildren _____ Great-Grandchildren _____

See Personal Profile, pages 42 to 45 for names and addresses of siblings, grandchildren, and great-grandchildren.

Cemetery

_____

Newspapers, professional and alumni newsletters, magazines and
organizations to send copies of this obituary:

Name _____

Address _____

Name _____

Address _____

Name _____

Address _____

Name _____

Address _____

Additional Information

_____

_____

_____

_____

_____

Date Prepared _____

Notes & Additions

Part 8

Executor Duties

" For God loveth a cheerful giver."

— II Corinthians 9:7

Wow! Being an executor is a lot of work!
I'm gonna have to think real hard
about who to name.
Maybe my kids won't want to?

Love,

Fannie ★

No Knowledge...

My husband, Charlie, and I live in Ohio and my only brother lived in Florida, so we didn't see each other much, and we certainly knew nothing of each other's affairs. Last spring we were passing through his area and decided to stop for a short visit. He was glad to see us, and he seemed his usual carefree self.

We arrived home two days later only to discover that my brother had died the day after we were there. Being his only surviving relatives, Charlie and I quickly returned to Florida to make arrangements and to try to finalize his estate.

What we found—or didn't find—was unbelievable, and still is. We searched the house for paperwork, bank statements, or documents of any kind. We found nothing! Nothing! We called all the banks and attorneys in the area, watched incoming mail for clues, and talked to neighbors and local churches. We discovered that his utility bills were always paid in cash at a local grocery store. The only income we could find was the monthly social security check, also cashed at the local grocery.

With no evidence of a will or any other documentation, we had no choice but to go home after three weeks of frustration. The estate (the house, car, and personal property) is now in the hands of the State of Florida legislature, to be settled and disbursed by the probate court to those entitled to it by Florida laws of descent.

Anonymous

"We have only one person to blame, and that's each other."
— Larry Breck

Legal Responsibilities

The executor is your personal representative **legally** responsible for settling your estate. The many duties of the executor involve making serious decisions regarding tax planning, management, and disbursement of your assets.

Who you appoint as executor is just as important as **who should accept** the responsibilities. Try to select someone who can meet the following criteria:

1. Willingness
2. Time
3. Competence

If there are no family members meeting this criteria, you may choose an attorney or a bank trust officer as an executor or co-executor. Also bear in mind that it is not unusual for even a well-organized estate to take several months or up to a year to settle.

The following is a "short list" of the legal responsibilities of the executor. For more detailed information, see Sources of Further Information on page 197 and check your local library for additional reference material.

1. Read the will. Find out if a last will and testament exists. (See page 97 or 101, Important Documents)
2. Make funeral arrangements, and obtain at least 10 copies of the death certificate.
3. Contact all interested parties, such as family, friends, employer, insurance agents, etc.
4. Petition the court for probate of the will. Contact the city or county court of the deceased's residence to obtain all necessary forms to "open the estate." The city clerk's office must be notified of filing letters of administration or letters testamentary, proving authority to settle the estate.
5. Keep orderly records of **all** information concerning the estate: transactions, vouchers, receipts, etc.
6. Assemble and inventory all assets. Determine what property is part of the estate, who are the parties likely to claim it, and what type of ownership exists. (See pages 71 or 75, Assets)

7. ADMINISTRATION

    a. Notify creditors such as mortgage and credit card companies, banks, utilities, etc. The legal "notice" form may be obtained from the courthouse. (See pages 68 to 70, Monthly and Periodic Bills)

    b. All available cash belonging to the deceased must be transferred to a newly opened estate bank account. Complete the collection of any income due, a search for all other assets, appraisal of real estate and personal property, and preparation and filing of the estate inventory.

    c. Process claims against the estate, and pay estate taxes.

    d. Business ownership by the deceased requires special consideration of the ramifications and liability to the executor. Legal counsel should help the executor determine his or her ability to run the business or whether it should be sold.

    e. Give written accounting to the court of all transactions made on behalf of the estate.

    f. Distribute the remainder of the estate to the heirs after taxes and claimants have been paid.

    g. Close the estate checking account and submit any necessary forms to legally close the estate.

8. Obtain final disclosure from the court.

This "short" list of executor responsibilities is intended for general guidance only. The author and publisher will not be responsible for any omissions. Seek competent legal advice pertaining to the user's primary state of residence.

Distribution of Personal Items 1

Instructions for the Executor of My Estate

for _____

IMPORTANT NOTE: The following information must be incorporated in your last will and testament to be enforceable. Upon completion of this section, consult with your attorney to have your will amended.

Pets

Example: Pet's Name: _*George (cat)*_____

    Name _*Jenny Smith*_____ Relationship _*Daughter*_____

1. Pet's Name _____

    Name _____ Relationship _____

2. Pet's Name _____

    Name _____ Relationship _____

Antiques

Example: Item: _*Walnut Basket Handmade by Great Grandfather in 1880*_____

    Name _*Joseph Smith*_____ Relationship _*Son*_____

1. Item _____

    Name _____ Relationship _____

2. Item _____

    Name _____ Relationship _____

3. Item _____

    Name _____ Relationship _____

4. Item _____

    Name _____ Relationship _____

Furniture

1. Item _____

    Name _____ Relationship _____

2. Item _____

    Name _____ Relationship _____

3. Item _____

   Name _____ Relationship _____

4. Item _____

   Name _____ Relationship _____

5. Item _____

   Name _____ Relationship _____

Jewelry

1. Item _____

   Name _____ Relationship _____

2. Item _____

   Name _____ Relationship _____

3. Item _____

   Name _____ Relationship _____

4. Item _____

   Name _____ Relationship _____

Guns

1. Item _____

   Name _____ Relationship _____

2. Item _____

   Name _____ Relationship _____

Automobiles

1. Item _____

   Name _____ Relationship _____

2. Item _____

   Name _____ Relationship _____

3. Item _____

   Name _____ Relationship _____

Clothing

1. Item _____

    Name _____ Relationship _____

2. Item _____

    Name _____ Relationship _____

3. Item _____

    Name _____ Relationship _____

Collectibles

1. Item _____

    Name _____ Relationship _____

2. Item _____

    Name _____ Relationship _____

3. Item _____

    Name _____ Relationship _____

4. Item _____

    Name _____ Relationship _____

Miscellaneous

1. Item _____

    Name _____ Relationship _____

2. Item _____

    Name _____ Relationship _____

3. Item _____

    Name _____ Relationship _____

4. Item _____

    Name _____ Relationship _____

5. Item _____

    Name _____ Relationship _____

6. Item _____

   Name _____ Relationship _____

7. Item _____

   Name _____ Relationship _____

8. Item _____

   Name _____ Relationship _____

9. Item _____

   Name _____ Relationship _____

10. Item _____

   Name _____ Relationship _____

11. Item _____

   Name _____ Relationship _____

12. Item _____

   Name _____ Relationship _____

13. Item _____

   Name _____ Relationship _____

14. Item _____

   Name _____ Relationship _____

15. Item _____

   Name _____ Relationship _____

16. Item _____

   Name _____ Relationship _____

17. Item _____

   Name _____ Relationship _____

18. Item _____

   Name _____ Relationship _____

19. Item _____

   Name _____ Relationship _____

20. Item _____

    Name _____ Relationship _____

21. Item _____

    Name _____ Relationship _____

22. Item _____

    Name _____ Relationship _____

23. Item _____

    Name _____ Relationship _____

24. Item _____

    Name _____ Relationship _____

25. Item _____

    Name _____ Relationship _____

26. Item _____

    Name _____ Relationship _____

27. Item _____

    Name _____ Relationship _____

28. Item _____

    Name _____ Relationship _____

29. Item _____

    Name _____ Relationship _____

30. Item _____

    Name _____ Relationship _____

31. Item _____

    Name _____ Relationship _____

32. Item _____

    Name _____ Relationship _____

33. Item _____

    Name _____ Relationship _____

34. Item _____

    Name _____ Relationship _____

35. Item _____

    Name _____ Relationship _____

36. Item _____

    Name _____ Relationship _____

37. Item _____

    Name _____ Relationship _____

38. Item _____

    Name _____ Relationship _____

39. Item _____

    Name _____ Relationship _____

40. Item _____

    Name _____ Relationship _____

41. Item _____

    Name _____ Relationship _____

42. Item _____

    Name _____ Relationship _____

"The greatest and perhaps the only perfect gift that we can give to the world is the gift of ourselves at our best."

— William N. Thomas

Date Prepared _____

Notes & Additions

Now don't you kids be fightin'
over this stuff—there's plenty to
go around—and I say who gets
what, you hear??

Love,

Fannie ★

Distribution of Personal Items 2

Instructions for the Executor of My Estate

for _____

IMPORTANT NOTE: The following information must be incorporated in your last will and testament to be enforceable. Upon completion of this section, consult with your attorney to have your will amended.

Pets

Example: Pet's Name: _____*George (cat)*_____

       Name _____*Jenny Smith*_____ Relationship *Daughter*_____

1. Pet's Name _____

       Name _____ Relationship _____

2. Pet's Name _____

       Name _____ Relationship _____

Antiques

Example: Item: _____*Walnut Basket Handmade by Great Grandfather in 1880*_____

       Name _____*Joseph Smith*_____ Relationship *Son*_____

1. Item _____

       Name _____ Relationship _____

2. Item _____

       Name _____ Relationship _____

3. Item _____

       Name _____ Relationship _____

4. Item _____

       Name _____ Relationship _____

Furniture

1. Item _____

       Name _____ Relationship _____

2. Item _____

       Name _____ Relationship _____

3. Item _____

   Name _____ Relationship _____

4. Item _____

   Name _____ Relationship _____

5. Item _____

   Name _____ Relationship _____

Jewelry

1. Item _____

   Name _____ Relationship _____

2. Item _____

   Name _____ Relationship _____

3. Item _____

   Name _____ Relationship _____

4. Item _____

   Name _____ Relationship _____

Guns

1. Item _____

   Name _____ Relationship _____

2. Item _____

   Name _____ Relationship _____

Automobiles

1. Item _____

   Name _____ Relationship _____

2. Item _____

   Name _____ Relationship _____

3. Item _____

   Name _____ Relationship _____

Clothing

1. Item _____
    Name _____ Relationship _____

2. Item _____
    Name _____ Relationship _____

3. Item _____
    Name _____ Relationship _____

Collectibles

1. Item _____
    Name _____ Relationship _____

2. Item _____
    Name _____ Relationship _____

3. Item _____
    Name _____ Relationship _____

4. Item _____
    Name _____ Relationship _____

Miscellaneous

1. Item _____
    Name _____ Relationship _____

2. Item _____
    Name _____ Relationship _____

3. Item _____
    Name _____ Relationship _____

4. Item _____
    Name _____ Relationship _____

5. Item _____
    Name _____ Relationship _____

6. Item _____

   Name _____ Relationship _____

7. Item _____

   Name _____ Relationship _____

8. Item _____

   Name _____ Relationship _____

9. Item _____

   Name _____ Relationship _____

10. Item _____

    Name _____ Relationship _____

11. Item _____

    Name _____ Relationship _____

12. Item _____

    Name _____ Relationship _____

13. Item _____

    Name _____ Relationship _____

14. Item _____

    Name _____ Relationship _____

15. Item _____

    Name _____ Relationship _____

16. Item _____

    Name _____ Relationship _____

17. Item _____

    Name _____ Relationship _____

18. Item _____

    Name _____ Relationship _____

19. Item _____

    Name _____ Relationship _____

20. Item _____

    Name _____ Relationship _____

21. Item _____

    Name _____ Relationship _____

22. Item _____

    Name _____ Relationship _____

23. Item _____

    Name _____ Relationship _____

24. Item _____

    Name _____ Relationship _____

25. Item _____

    Name _____ Relationship _____

26. Item _____

    Name _____ Relationship _____

27. Item _____

    Name _____ Relationship _____

28. Item _____

    Name _____ Relationship _____

29. Item _____

    Name _____ Relationship _____

30. Item _____

    Name _____ Relationship _____

31. Item _____

    Name _____ Relationship _____

32. Item _____

    Name _____ Relationship _____

33. Item _____

    Name _____ Relationship _____

34. Item _____

    Name _____ Relationship _____

35. Item _____

    Name _____ Relationship _____

36. Item _____

    Name _____ Relationship _____

37. Item _____

    Name _____ Relationship _____

38. Item _____

    Name _____ Relationship _____

39. Item _____

    Name _____ Relationship _____

40. Item _____

    Name _____ Relationship _____

41. Item _____

    Name _____ Relationship _____

42. Item _____

    Name _____ Relationship _____

Date Prepared _____

Notes & Additions

Part 9

Family History

"Therefore comfort one another
with these words."

— I Thessalonians 4:18 (NAS)

God even blesses clowns! I've had some great times and wonderful memories. As a child who was your hero? What would you like to be remembered for? Now don't make stuff up!

Better write them down for the grandchildren. They'll have a real hoot!

Love,

★

Fannie

About Family Stories

In 1879 my great-grandmother received a very large, very beautiful, leather-bound Bible as a wedding gift. Lovingly, she began recording family events: births, deaths, marriages, and clippings from the local newspaper of family members involved in popular social events of that era, such as afternoon teas. The Bible was handed down to the next generation, and grandmother continued the tradition, adding her own stories and style to this wonderful tradition.

When my grandmother died, instructions were that the Bible be left in the possession of the oldest living son, and, after several years, my father joyfully received the Bible. By then, however, the tradition of adding family events and stories had sadly long since died.

I never tire of reading those old stories or of hearing my father tell stories of his life during childhood and the World Wars. My family is encouraging him to continue the tradition—to get the stories recorded for us and for our children and our children's children.

Many people today don't even know their great-grandparent's names, much less the treasured stories of their lives. No wonder so many of us don't know who we are—we don't know where we came from! We are unable to acknowledge the strength of character, bravery and heroism, the accomplishments or the spirit of our ancestors.

Now is your chance to begin, or continue, a valuable family tradition for the benefit of the generations to come. Imagine your future generations sitting quietly one hundred years from now, reading your stories with tears of joy or sadness and feeling so thankful that you took the time to let them know who you are and where they came from.

Elaine Todd

" Write things which thou hast seen, and the things which are..."
— Revelation 1:19

Family Tree

Four-Generation Chart of Husband

Compiled by _____

b = birth, date, and place
m = marriage, date, and place
d = death, date, and place

b   m   d

b   m   d

b   m   d

b   m   d

Spouse

b   m   d

b   m   d

b   m   d

b   m   d

b   m   d

b   m   d

b   m   d

b   m   d

b   m   d

b   m   d

b   m   d

b   m   d

b   m   d

b   m   d

b   m   d

b   m   d

b   m   d

b   m   d

b   m   d

b   m   d

b   m   d

b   m   d

b   m   d

b   m   d

b   m   d

b   m   d

b   m   d

Family Tree

Four-Generation Chart of Wife

Complied by _____

b = birth, date, and place
m = marriage, date, and place
d = death, date, and place

b   m   d

b   m   d

b   m   d

Spouse

b   m   d

b   m   d

b   m   d

b   m   d

b   m   d

b   m   d

b   m   d

b   m   d

b   m   d

b   m   d

b   m   d

b   m   d

b   m   d

b   m   d

b   m   d

b   m   d

b   m   d

b   m   d

b   m   d

Family Stories

Story Title _____

_____

_____

_____

_____

_____

_____

_____

_____

_____

_____

_____

_____

_____

_____

_____

_____

_____

_____

_____

_____

_____

Source of Story _____

Origination Date _____

Family Stories

Story Title _____

_____

_____

_____

_____

_____

_____

_____

_____

_____

_____

_____

_____

_____

_____

_____

_____

_____

_____

_____

_____

_____

Source of Story _____

Origination Date _____

Family Stories

Story Title _____

_____

_____

_____

_____

_____

_____

_____

_____

_____

_____

_____

_____

_____

_____

_____

_____

_____

_____

_____

_____

_____

_____

Source of Story _____

Origination Date _____

Family Stories

Story Title _____

_____

_____

_____

_____

_____

_____

_____

_____

_____

_____

_____

_____

_____

_____

_____

_____

_____

_____

_____

_____

Source of Story _____

Origination Date _____

Family Stories

Story Title _____

_____

_____

_____

_____

_____

_____

_____

_____

_____

_____

_____

_____

_____

_____

_____

_____

_____

_____

_____

_____

_____

_____

_____

Source of Story _____

Origination Date _____

Family Stories

Story Title _____

_____

_____

_____

_____

_____

_____

_____

_____

_____

_____

_____

_____

_____

_____

_____

_____

_____

_____

_____

_____

Source of Story _____

Origination Date _____

Family Stories

Story Title _____

_____

_____

_____

_____

_____

_____

_____

_____

_____

_____

_____

_____

_____

_____

_____

_____

_____

_____

_____

_____

Source of Story _____

Origination Date _____

Notes & Additions

Notes & Additions

Part 10

Further Information

"... Always giving thanks to God
the Father for everything ... "
— Ephesians 5:20 (NIV)

You did it! ★

Congratulations

That wasn't so bad was it? ★

Love and hugs,

★ Fannie

Sources of Additional Information

Christianson, Stephen G., Esq. *How to Administer an Estate.* New London, CT: Citadel Press, 1993.

Equitable Foundation, Inc., and Children of Aging Parents. *Aging Parents and Common Sense: A Practical Guide for You and Your Parents.* CAPS, 1996. Free; call (800) 227-7294.

Harley, Gordon, "How to Protect Your Life Savings From Catastrophic Illness and Nursing Homes". Boston, MA: Financial Strategies Press, Inc.

National Association of Insurance Commissioners. *A Shoppers Guide to Long-Term Care Insurance.* NAIC, 1990.

Palder, Edward L. *The Retirement Sourcebook.* Kensington, MD: Woodbine House, 1989.

Petras, Kathryn, and Ross Petras. *The Only Retirement Guide You'll Ever Need.* New York, NY: Poseidon Press, 1991.

Plotnick, Charles K., LL.B., and Leimberg, Stephan R., J.D. *How to Settle an Estate.* Bridgeport, CT: Consumer Reports Books, 1991.

Purdue University. *The Peace of Mind Program.* West Lafayette, Indiana: Purdue University, Development Office, School of Veterinary Medicine, 1996.

Runde, Robert H., and Zischang, J. Barry. *The Common Sense Guide to Estate Planning.* Burr Ridge, IL: Business One Irwin, 1994.

Schomaker, Mary Zimmeth. *How One Night Changed Five Lives.* Far Hills, NJ: New Horizon Press, 1996.

Suski, D. Helen. *Hiring Home Caregivers.* San Luis Obispo, CA: American Source Books, 1995.

Notes & Additions

Letter of Notification

Date: _____

From: _____

To: _____

Dear _____,

IMPORTANT INFORMATION! I have recorded personal preferences and wishes, as well as medical and financial information, in a book titled *All Together Now.* In case of my DISABILITY or DEATH, refer to this book immediately for instructions and guidance. It will save you a tremendous amount of time and anguish.

Please respect that some of this information is CONFIDENTIAL and should be shared only with those named below:

Name _____

Name _____

You will find my book, *All Together Now* in:

_____

_____

Quick reference emergency information is as follows:

I am a member of MEDIC ALERT (800) 825-3785	Yes ____	No ____
I wish to be an ORGAN and TISSUE DONOR (800) 355-SHARE	Yes ____	No ____
I have a LIVING WILL	Yes ____	No ____
I have chosen a POWER OF ATTORNEY FOR HEALTHCARE	Yes ____	No ____

This book was completed with considerable effort, much love and respect for those who will be picking up the pieces of my life. Thank you for honoring my trust.

Sincerely,

_____

Signature